"Holley Moseley shows how the inspiring love of one family can drive policy reform to help millions. From the adoption of a special needs child to the legislative adoption of cannabis reform deemed politically impossible, Holley wins by appealing to the best compassions within us. Her family's challenges changed the votes and vetoes of legislators and governors. Their triumphs will inspire the cannabis reform movement forever. Her story is a roadmap to better policy-making, driven by a unifying, bipartisan desire to help the vulnerable with love and focused common purpose."

—Congressman Matt Gaetz

"An inspiring journey of a mother's unstoppable pursuit to give her child the best life possible despite challenging medical conditions. In sharing her story, Holley's experience and advocacy will help many other parents navigate the use of cannabis as medicine."

—Bonni Goldstein, MD

"This is a remarkable story of family, love, and perseverance. I was lucky enough to witness this story as it unfolded and to be a part of the important work that was done to make this incredible treatment an option for families all over our great state of Florida. As a father myself, advocating for families has always been an important corner-stone of my career, and being able to help kids like RayAnn is one of the greatest joys in my work. Holley has done a remarkable job of using this book to not only tell her story, but to provide other parents with advice and solutions that will help them to navigate their own journeys. Parents everywhere should read this book for a real-life take on life with a special needs child and an inspiring story of what the love of a parent can truly accomplish."

—Senator Rob Bradley

A RAY OF HOPE

A mother's story

of love, healing,

and the miracle of

medical marijuana

HOLLEY MOSELEY

Published by:
Hope Grows Publishing
P.O. Box 991
Gulf Breeze, FL 32562
850-232-0004
www.arayofhopebook.com

ISBN: 978-0-692-13847-2

Library of Congress Control Number: 2018954961

Printed in the United States of America

To RayAnn, Presley, and Gabrielle.

There is no greater joy than being your mother.

Table of Contents

Foreword

Physicians know that no two cases will ever be the same. We approach each day, each patient, and each diagnosis with a fresh set of eyes and expectations. So when I met RayAnn Moseley and her mother, Holley, in 2008, I never imagined that our relationship would extend beyond one of neurologist and patient. Yet what has unfolded since then is a partnership that changed the course of my career and the lives of countless patients.

RayAnn Moseley, who happens to live with epilepsy, is a beautiful child. Something about her personality just draws you in. She is lively and engaging and always seems to exude happiness, even at her most desperately ill. At least that is how I perceived her when I first started treating her as a young girl. But when I saw her again years later at Holley's request, there had been a noticeable change in her demeanor.

At that time RayAnn was on a high dose of several different anti-seizure medications but was continuing to experience frequent, debilitating seizures. Worse, she was listless and withdrawn—not at all the vivacious young girl I had once met. I was shocked and dismayed by the devastating effects of the medications. Not only were they no longer working to treat her symptoms; they were taking away the very essence of RayAnn.

This time, Holley had brought RayAnn to me hoping to find a viable alternative to her daughter's current treatment plan. So we began strategizing some different ways to treat RayAnn's symptoms. First, we reduced the current medications in hopes of lessening some of the debilitating side effects. We had some success with this course of treatment at first, but after several months, RayAnn's health became worse. Once again, I found myself sitting across from a mother desperate for answers.

It was around this time that Holley broached the subject of using CBD oil (more specifically, Charlotte's Web) as a treatment for RayAnn. As a physician and researcher, I was compelled to answer her honestly: I knew very little about it. Frankly, there wasn't much research to indicate what CBD oil might achieve in a patient like RayAnn, or what side effects might ensue. However, I had read enough to know that it was a path worth exploring.

Today, as you will discover when you read this book, RayAnn is seizure-free and no longer suffers from the debilitating side effects of the high-powered medications she once depended on. She is an active teenager who is full of life and personality. The real RayAnn is back.

In hindsight, I'm also grateful that Holley didn't allow my lack of expertise on the subject of CBD oil to quell her determination. I have found there are few forces more powerful than a mother's will to fight on behalf of her sick child. Holley read everything she could get her hands on and talked to everyone she could. She asked the questions and did the research. She became deeply informed on the topic, quickly exceeding my own knowledge.

I have learned a great deal from Holley and regularly refer my patients to her as a resource to help them get started. She directs them to the best products to use and helps them feel more comfortable about pursuing this unorthodox (and highly controversial) course of action.

Since Holley came into my office that day asking about using CBD oil to treat epilepsy, we have done some exciting research and seen promising results. We have every reason to believe this treatment will benefit children and adults who suffer from a variety of diagnoses. Every day, as we continue to research and gain knowledge, the possibilities for treatment are growing. This is deeply encouraging.

Yet even more striking than the insights I've gained from reading about the science and the legislation around CBD oil is what I've learned from Holley and other parents like her. Once they saw that "ray of hope," they fought hard. They advocated tirelessly. They won some remarkable victories, most notably when the Compassionate Medical Cannabis Act of 2014 was passed in Florida, making this treatment legally available to their daughter and other patients like her. It truly doesn't get any better than this.

I often tell people, both inside the medical community and out, "You may think you're an expert, but it's the parents who *really* know." Ordinary parents are the ones who got it right and who continue to get it right. They keep pushing for acceptance of a medication that's greatly misunderstood and demonized. They have forced many intelligent and experienced professionals to rethink how they treat patients and how they view the forces that shape the world of science and the political machine.

These parents have taught us things we couldn't have learned in medical school, or anywhere else. They aren't lobbyists or industry stakeholders. They aren't seeking political or financial gain. They are simply parents looking for answers and trying to give their children a better quality of life and a healthier future. The power of these parents—their love and devotion to their kids and their strength and determination—is a story that deserves to be recognized. Without them, we wouldn't be where we are today.

The story you are about to read is remarkable in many ways. It contains valuable take-aways for parents and patients alike, and I hope you will find them helpful. But mostly I hope you'll read between the lines of this story and appreciate Holley's heroism. Her diligence and refusal to give up led to a solution for RayAnn and paved the way for countless other families to have the same. She has inspired me, and I hope she inspires you, too.

Never stop searching, never stop learning, and never stop fighting.

—Paul R. Carney, MD, Professor of Neurology and Pediatrics Department of Neurology, University of North Carolina at Chapel Hill

Acknowledgments

"For I know the plans I have for you," declares the Lord, "plans to prosper you and not to harm you, plans to give you hope and a future." Jeremiah 29:11

I want to start by thanking God. Thank you for having a plan grander than I could have ever imagined. I am so grateful that I followed.

To my husband, Peyton—Thank you for how hard you work for our family. We love you!

Presley, my son—From the moment I found out I was pregnant, I was head over heels for you. Thank you for being a loving brother to your sisters.

Gabrielle, my daughter, the baby—You are one of a kind. Thank you for your compassion and confidence. Thank you for filling in and helping care for RayAnn.

My parents, John and Jackie Heller—Thank you for supporting me through good times and bad. I know that I can always count on you. Thank you for all you have done for my kids. We could not have done it without you.

My sisters, Lindsey and Amanda—There is a saying "Having sisters means you always have backup," and this could not be more true for us. Thank you for always having my back.

Jane "MiMi" Moseley, mother-in-law—For always being eager and willing to help with the kids.

Dr. Robin Renfroe, pediatrician—Thank you for listening to my concerns, for being a diligent and thorough physician, and supporting my choices (even when it sounded as crazy as medical cannabis).

Dr. Paul Carney—Thank you for saving RayAnn's life! RayAnn was at her worst when we first came to see you. I am so grateful that you heard our concerns and advocated for a better quality of life for RayAnn.

Wendy Sheehan, ARNP, at UF Health Shands—Thank you for your calm presence.

Dr. Minh Le—Thank you for helping us obtain RayAnn's genetic testing. We are forever grateful for your kindness!

Teachers, Mrs. Angela Pettus and Mrs. Margaret Shirley—Some days you spent more time with RayAnn than I did. Thank you for loving her like your own!

Gulf Breeze community—How blessed we are to live in this community. We can not thank you enough for your support of RayAnn and our family.

To all who helped with the "Rally for RayAnn" fundraiser—Thank you!

Teresa Eckles—Thank you for sharing your experience and wisdom during difficult times.

St. Ann Discovery School—Thank you for accepting RayAnn into your daycare when no one else would. Thank you for not being afraid of her diagnosis and instead saw her as a child of God.

GBUMC—Our second home! Thank you for sharing God's love with my kids.

Northwest Florida Clinical Research Group—Thank you for being understanding and lenient of a mother trying to work while caring for a special needs child.

Sacred Heart Hospital PICU staff—Thank you for taking care of RayAnn during some of her worst times.

Quint Studer—Thank you for providing transportation for RayAnn when she was unable to fly commercial. Thank you for seeing the need for epilepsy services in our community and acting on it!

Shriners Hospitals for Children, Tampa—Thank you for providing orthopedic care to RayAnn.

Make-A-Wish Foundation—Thank you for granting RayAnn's wish to meet the Disney princesses.

Thank you to all of RayAnn's speech therapists, occupational therapists, and physical therapists.

Paige and Charlotte Figi—Thank you for being brave enough to share Charlotte's story with the world.

Dr. Sanjay Gupta—Thank you for filming the CNN documentary *Weed* and publicly changing your view on medical cannabis.

You have changed so many lives because you followed the science and not the stigma.

Stanley brothers—Thank you for creating Charlotte's Web and helping families obtain access.

Thank you to all who helped pass the Compassionate Medical Cannabis Act of 2014. I would like to thank the bill sponsors—Representative Matt Gaetz, Representative Katie Edwards, Senator Rob Bradley, Senator Aaron Bean, and Senator Jeff Brandes. I would like to thank our fearless lobbyists, Jules Kariher and Kim Bertron, as well as our media consultant, Ryan Wiggins.

I would like to thank every senator and representative who took time to meet with us and listen to our *why*.

Media played a *huge* role in the success of this bill. I would like to thank all the reporters who shared our story and helped to educate the public of the need for CBD-rich oil in Florida.

I would also like to thank Governor Rick Scott for keeping his word and signing the bill.

Caring 4 Florida board members—Thank you for your time, support, and guidance.

Ray of Hope, LLC—Thank you for sharing our vision and making it a reality.

I would like to thank Saphira Galoob, lobbyist and friend—For her medical cannabis advocacy efforts on the federal level.

I want to thank everyone who helped work on this book. The hours of editing drafts and preparing layouts has paid off. This is a dream come true!

**RayAnn—Last but not least, to you…the one who inspired this all! Thank you for being YOU!

Part 1

Chapter 1

There's a saying I've often heard about how if you want to make God laugh, you can just tell Him your plans. I've always been a planner. I had my future planned out to a "T." But you see, the thing about life is you can't plan for everything. And it's often the times your life goes the furthest off script that the best moments happen: the surprises, the unexpected, the miracles. It's funny how life works—looking back at the decisions you've made, the paths you've chosen, how they end up leading you right to the place you were always meant to be. And one day, when you look back on the story that's been written in the days and weeks that follow, you see how it all fell into place despite the things you *thought* you were planning for at the time. And maybe then you'll find yourself laughing, too.

As the oldest of three girls, I had spent a lot of my childhood watching over my younger siblings. It seemed I had always been drawn to the role of caregiver, and I had a heart for working with children—a career in nursing seemed like a natural fit.

I had always been drawn to the role of caregiver, and I had a heart for working with children.

It was the summer of 2004. I was fresh off the life-changing experience of nursing school at the University of South Alabama. I had spent late nights and early mornings learning the ins and outs of my life's calling; heart rhythms and hospital clinicals and patient care plans had filled my days and prepared me for my future as a nurse. I had found my groove inside the walls of the NICU, PICU, and pediatric floors of the hospitals where I was learning. It became clear to me early on that pediatrics was where I belonged. I had a special heart for the special cases—the tough ones that are hard to take on and stick with you long after they are over. You see, sick kids have a different outlook as patients. They don't whine as much or bemoan their circumstances—they are fighters.

Sick kids have a different outlook as patients...they are fighters.

That summer was full of change. My fiancé, Peyton, graduated from the radiology technician program at my alma mater. We were married on August 14, 2004, in front of 250 of our closest friends and family. Upon returning home from our tropical honeymoon, we packed up our lives and moved from our home in Pensacola to Cape Coral, Florida, where Peyton had been accepted to the Radiation Therapy Program. In a whirlwind, we bought our first home together, I took my nursing boards, and I accepted a position at the Children's Hospital of Southwest Florida in Fort Myers. We had no way of knowing at the time, but we were traveling down the path that would prepare us and eventually lead us right to the moment that would change our lives forever.

When I look back at our story, I feel an overwhelming sense of gratitude that this is where God led us first. I delighted in my new career. I learned so much from the nurses I was working with at the hospital. They gave me the invaluable gift of confidence in myself—a vital part of being a great nurse. I enjoyed working with my patients—and there were several children during this time who left a permanent mark on my heart. In nursing school, we were taught time and again that the golden rule was always to keep a distance from our patients. If we could keep our distance, we could keep our heads clear and that would allow us to offer the best care possible. It was a rule I never could seem to make myself follow, especially in my work with pediatric patients. In fact, I found the exact opposite to be true. I had to be close to my patients—to show them love and compassion—in order to care for them the way they needed.

It was around this time that my new husband and I began to day-dream together about the next phase of our future—starting a family. We set goals of steady jobs and living near family—and I floated the idea of international adoption. I knew from pretty early on that I could fall in love with a child who wasn't biologically my own. In fact, I had always been drawn to the idea of adoption long before starting my own family was even a consideration. While Peyton wasn't imme-diately on board about the idea, I knew it was something I felt led to explore. We agreed to slow down and take things one step at a time. There would be plenty of time for figuring it all out later (or so we thought—do you hear God laughing yet?).

I knew from early on that I could fall in love with a child who wasn't biologically my own. I was drawn to adoption.

Peyton finished up his classes, and our time in Cape Cor-al came to an end. I was sad to leave our first home together as a couple and my first real hospital "home" but also looked forward to setting down roots in our hometown of Pensacola. We moved home and started new jobs: Peyton at Sacred Heart Hospital in the Cancer Center and me at the Children's Hospital at Sacred Heart on the school age/adolescent floor working with children ages five and older. Each day I saw a varying degree of disease and illnesses in my young patients. I also had the opportunity to accept a PRN position ("as needed") with the Child Neurology Center located inside the hospital. At the Neurology Center I was assisting with nursing calls and procedures and learning something new every single day. Every piece of the puzzle—a puzzle I wasn't aware I was putting together, mind you—was starting to fall into place. We were being prepared for something big, the greatest adventure of our lives. We just hadn't met her yet.

Chapter 2

It was 5:30 a.m. on the day my life would change forever. I got ready for work, putting on my scrubs and heading out the door to work a 12-hour shift at the hospital. It was an ordinary day in every way, except, unbeknownst to me, it was a day that would be unlike any other.

After checking in with the night nurse and receiving her report, I surveyed the list of patients I was assigned to for that day. Among them was a medical shelter patient—this is a child who is currently in the foster system who has a medical condition and does not have a current placement inside a medical foster home. When this happens, these children are brought to the hospital to stay until a home can be located, so that their medical needs can be properly attended to.

On that particular day, there were a total of four medical shelter children in the hospital, and I was assigned to one of them.

I reviewed the report for the medical shelter patient on my roster. Her name was RayAnn. She had been removed from her parents due to neglect. She was diagnosed with cerebral palsy and epilepsy and had not been receiving her anti-seizure medications. Little else was known, other than that she came in with a baby bottle and was unable to walk on her own. I reviewed her chart and medication administration record (MAR) and learned that she was only two years old. This surprised me at first, because our unit typically included only children ages five and up—but in this case, the infant/toddler unit was full, and so this patient was admitted to our unit. At the time, on that ordinary day, none of these facts seemed out of place to me; I did not feel the divine providence as it was happening or feel the magical hand of fate guiding me toward her door. But now, as I look back on our story and how it happened, I know there was a reason that day played out the way it did.

I peeked in her room and saw a small figure sleeping in a crib with a tent on it (a device used to prevent her from climbing out). She was alone in the room, sleeping peacefully. After a quick glance around to make sure all was well, I left her door cracked and went on my way to check on my other patients.

At the time, on that ordinary day, I did not feel the divine providence as it was happening. But now, as I look back on our story, I know there was a reason it happened the way it did.

After making my rounds, I made my way back around to her. As I peeked back into the room, I saw that she was now awake and sitting up in her crib. She was not fussing or crying—she just sat quietly and looked at me as I walked in. I asked her if she wanted to eat breakfast and brought her food tray over. I noticed her soft blonde hair and captivating blue eyes. She was of average weight and height for her age but had poor muscle control. I began feeding her breakfast. She had a healthy appetite but had difficulty chewing and swallowing her food—but we kept at it and she ate every bite of her pancakes, sausage, and fruit. As I fed her, I noticed that she enjoyed the one-on-one attention and began to let her guard down the more we interacted. After administering her morning meds, I found a nursing student to pull her around the halls in a red wagon. As she did, I couldn't help but notice that everyone she passed would stop in the hallways to say "hi" to her. There was just something about her that drew people in.

At the end of my shift, I popped in and told RayAnn goodbye and that I would be back in the morning. She seemed comfortable in her crib watching TV, but there was something in me that hated leaving her there all alone. The next morning, I was excited to get to work and check on RayAnn. I was even more excited when I found out that I was going to be her nurse again. I administered her morning anti-seizure medication and asked the student nurses to take her to the "playroom" so she could move around and be a kid. I went in periodically and checked on her whenever I got the chance. She was not steady on her feet but was determined to get around. *She may be small but she's got spunk*, I thought to myself. *A fighter.*

With another 12-hour shift looming the following day, I reluctantly said my good-byes and headed home, and still I felt that nagging feeling about leaving RayAnn. I settled on the couch with my drive-thru taco dinner, and my mind drifted back to the blue-eyed girl back at the hospital. The house seemed quiet. Too quiet. *We have three unused rooms in this house*, I thought to myself. *We have a jungle gym in our backyard for crying out loud.* I sat the taco down with determination. I decided then and there that it was time for Peyton and me to talk again about expanding our family.

The next morning when I entered RayAnn's hospital room, she was excited to see me. I gave her a big hug and felt encouraged. We spent most of that day roaming the halls in the red wagon—by then everyone knew her by name and greeted her. She was so well behaved and hardly ever fussed. She glowed under the attention she was receiving (and the staff loved giving it to her). We would allow her to sit in her red wagon with the receptionist in the nurse's station, after the student nurses left, so she wouldn't have to be in her hospital room alone. The entire staff was falling for this little girl, but nobody was falling harder than I was. That night, it was even harder to leave her. I met my husband for dinner and we talked about our days. I told him a little bit about RayAnn.

The entire staff was falling for this little girl, but nobody was falling harder than I was.

The next day, I tried to sleep in (because three 12-hour shifts will take it out of you), but instead I was up early thinking about RayAnn and unable to go back to sleep. My mind raced with questions: *Who is her nurse today? Are student nurses there to play with her? Is she going to be stuck in her crib all day?* Enough was enough—I gave up on sleep and jumped out of bed. I decided to run into Target and get her an outfit and a pair of shoes, and go have lunch with her.

When I arrived in her room, she stood up in her crib and was visibly excited to see me. As I was feeding her lunch, I found myself wishing that she didn't have to eat hospital food every day. I put her new shoes (white with pink flowers!) on her and took her through the halls for a walk. I gave her a hug and an extra little squeeze in case she was not there when I returned for my next shift, which was still several days away.

In the days between shifts, I found myself thinking and praying about her often. *Dear God, please wrap RayAnn in your arms. Bless her with a good medical foster home. Heal her and allow her to continue to make progress. Amen.* But to my surprise when I returned to work, RayAnn was still there. Part of me was selfishly happy—I would get to spend more time with her! On that day, I took her across the hall to visit the Child Neurology Center, where my mom, Jackie, worked. As it turned out, my mom had known RayAnn from the time she was a baby—she had been a patient in their office since she was born. The neurologist there also knew RayAnn well and told me a little bit about her seizure history. The little toddler in my arms had spent her infant life in and out of the hospital. I couldn't imagine this as I looked at the relatively healthy girl in front of me. She may have been unable to walk on her own and struggled with coordination, but her seizures seemed to be stable and she was improving every day. My gut was telling me that if she could be under stable care, she would make great strides. I prayed again that night for a good medical foster home.

> I found myself thinking and praying about her often. Dear God, please wrap RayAnn in your arms. Bless her with a good medical foster home. Heal her and allow her to continue to make progress. Amen.

On my next shift at work, I spoke with the social worker about RayAnn. She told me that while she had found a home for one of the other medical foster patients, she hadn't been able to find anything for RayAnn. It was December and Christmas was rapidly approaching, and I couldn't stand the thought of RayAnn spending Christmas alone in the hospital. It's sad enough for any child to have to spend the holidays in a hospital—but it felt especially devastating for a child who was well enough to *be* home but just didn't have one to go to. I put all my doubts and fears aside and asked the social worker how I could help—was it possible for RayAnn to stay with us until a medical foster home could be found? As the words came out of my mouth, I wasn't thinking about what all it would take—we didn't have anything at our home for a two- year-old. We weren't even approved to be foster parents! It was just a shot in the dark—a desperate plea to help the blue-eyed girl who had stolen my heart. "Have you heard of non-relative placement?" she asked. They were the words that were about to change my life forever. "We would have to get her parents to sign off on it, but it is an option. If you are serious, I can pursue this." I didn't hesitate. Not even for a second. "Let's do this," I said. "I just need to get my husband's approval first."

Since Peyton worked just downstairs in the Cancer Center, I asked him to come visit RayAnn on his lunch break. He didn't say much, didn't ask questions, or wonder aloud what I was up to. He simply said, "Okay." Years later, after all was said and done, he admitted to me that he never thought any of it was going to work out anyway (and truthfully, I wasn't sure myself!)—he had just been trying to make me happy.

Over that next week, I worked closely with the social worker as she got approval from RayAnn's parents for her to be placed in non-relative placement with us. We completed a home study, got financial approval, got mental health approval; the paperwork and litany of red tape seemed endless. The week of Christmas was upon us. We had one week to make this happen or she would have to spend Christmas in a hospital room. I took time off work and completed all that was needed for our application, and, finally, miraculously, we were approved.

In a flurry of excitement, my mom, sister, mother-in-law, and I spent an afternoon shopping to stock up on all things little girl—we bought clothes, shoes, diapers, a car seat, and a toddler bed. We loaded our carts with sippie cups, kid dishes, baby-proof items, and toys.

I picked up her medications from the pharmacy. I couldn't believe the support that I was receiving. Everyone was embracing this. We were not overthinking the "what-ifs" but just doing the next right thing. We were letting our hearts lead us. I didn't feel a moment of anxiety or regret. I knew that my prayers were being answered. *We* were the foster family that RayAnn needed at that time, and while she was with us, we would love her and spoil her. We would help her grow and hit developmental milestones. I barely slept all night. I was so excited. I felt only happy excitement and anticipation—not a moment of anxiety or regret. RayAnn was coming home.

I arrived at the hospital early. RayAnn needed an EEG before she could be discharged. (An EEG, or electroencephalogram, is a test that detects the electrical activity in the brain.) I went with her to the EEG lab and held her while she was connected to the EEG electrodes. She fussed some because she did not like having her head messed with, but I knew that this procedure would not hurt her. After she was connected, I laid with her in the bed trying to get her to stay still and rest. She was not interested. This was the first time I remember feeling something different inside of me. I am a nurse—I am used to being in a hospital, doing medical procedures on patients, holding children down while they cry. But this time, I was here as RayAnn's caretaker and I wanted to shelter her from any unneeded stress.

When the test was over, we were taken back to her room to pack up RayAnn's few things and sign her discharge paperwork. She was finally free. The nurses and staff said their good-byes, and we set off on our new adventure.

As we walked outside to the car, I noticed RayAnn as she seemed to marvel at the fresh air, and it hit me that she had been stuck inside for so long that she likely had forgotten what it felt like to be outdoors. We got her into her new car seat and headed home. She seemed at ease. She didn't fuss or look worried; she just took it all in.

We arrived at home and gave her a bath and had lunch. We then let her explore around our house and meet the dogs. She seemed very comfortable—almost as if she knew she was home.

We settled in nicely—our families loved RayAnn and couldn't stay away. She seemed comfortable in our home, and we enjoyed playing with her and watching her explore. I continued to work diligently on the to-do list that the social worker had given to me—scheduling appointments and finding her a daycare. Christmas was a whirlwind. We visited with family and enjoyed showering RayAnn with presents. We took photos on the front porch and it felt like we were a little family. I didn't allow myself to think about how long she would be with us. I just soaked up every minute that we had.

I didn't allow myself to think about how long she would be with us. I just soaked up every minute that we had.

RayAnn continued to do very well. She was adjusting to living with Peyton and me. She attended speech, occupational, and physical therapy sessions twice a week at Sacred Heart Hospital outpatient therapy. She was established with a pediatrician. We had her first orthopedic appointment, and the physician recommended RayAnn be fitted for AFOs (leg braces). She now walked around in cool pink and purple orthotics. She saw her pediatric neurologist, and we agreed that she was stable and no changes to her medication were necessary. RayAnn received Botox in her legs for spasticity. (Botox is not FDA-approved for the treatment of spasticity in children under the age of 18 years old and is also not approved for lower limb spasticity. As we would come to learn, many of the treatments prescribed for RayAnn through the years would fall under this category.) We bought her a new canopy bed and painted her room pink. She attended birthday parties. We spent our weekends with family at the beach or out on the boat.

We also had to make weekly visitations with her biological parents and brother. Her brother was only four years old at the time. He was diagnosed with autism and was placed in a foster home with a special needs school teacher. At most of the visitation appointments, RayAnn's father did not attend and her mother would either show up late or leave early. After a few months of driving the 30 minutes back and forth, I became very frustrated. Why was I going out of my way? Why were her parents not trying? Do they not want their children back? I wondered often if RayAnn and her brother were already where they were meant to be.

As part of their case, a judge had explained to RayAnn's biological parents that they needed to attend RayAnn's therapy appointments to prove that they could continue them if they wanted to get her back. At one of the therapy sessions, RayAnn's biological mother showed up with a social worker. As part of the appointment, the physical therapist asked RayAnn to walk to her mom to show her how hard she had been working. Her biological mother was sitting on a bench in the therapy room, and I was sitting next to her. With all of her tiny determination, RayAnn stumbled over and reached for me. I didn't know how to react. I hugged RayAnn and tried to pass her over, but I knew it hurt her mother's feelings, and because of that, she left the appointment. She never attended another one after that day.

At the next appointment, the social worker attended without RayAnn's biological parents. He pulled me to the side and told me more of RayAnn's story. Until then, I had known only bits and pieces. Hearing the tragic details of her story made me feel faint. I felt like walking to the bathroom to vomit but I was worried that I would not make it. So I just sat in my chair, feeling pale and dizzy. I had heard some pretty disgusting stories and seen some pretty tragic situations working in the hospital, but because I had feelings for this child, I couldn't think straight. I went home and Peyton and I talked, and we decided to find the best attorney in town. RayAnn could not go back to that home. She was thriving socially, medically, and physically, and we would do everything in our power to make sure it stayed that way.

We continued moving forward, taking RayAnn to experience new things. The zoo was one of her favorite places, and she loved the giraffes. She began ballet lessons. She thrived and our love for her grew.

We appeared in court on October 26, 2006, with our attorney. RayAnn had been in our care for almost one year. We brought in scrapbooks filled with memories. I wanted the judge to see our love for RayAnn. Before our case was called in, I ran into RayAnn's biological mother and she asked to see the scrapbook. I felt nervous but we sat down next to each other and flipped through the pages. Each page was filled with photographs of RayAnn smiling and playing—pictures at the beach, at the park, at school. Photos of RayAnn with our friends and family. I noticed that she was smiling and seemed to be enjoying looking through the photographs. I hoped that she could see that we loved RayAnn as our own and would take care of her. Through everything, I had felt a lot of anger toward RayAnn's biological mother for what had happened to RayAnn. But watching her smiling as she flipped through the photographs shifted something in me, and my heart softened toward her that day.

Some weeks later, I had a dream that I was out with friends and was wearing a tight black dress, and several people came up and congratulated me on being pregnant. But in the dream, I wasn't pregnant and I didn't look pregnant. I woke up and laughed it off. I got RayAnn ready and dropped her off at school. The dream was nagging at me, so I stopped by the drug store to pick up a pregnancy test. When I got home, I took the test and couldn't believe my eyes. Two pink lines. My dream had been right! I was actually pregnant. I was so excited— things weren't exactly happening how we had planned but here we were. I threw on my coat and went to surprise Peyton at work. He was as surprised and delighted as I was. After he caught his breath, we hugged and kissed. I asked him to keep it a secret until I could go to the doctor and confirm it. I wanted us to tell RayAnn and our parents together.

On April 13, 2007, Presley John Moseley was born. He was the spitting image of his father and a big boy weighing in at 9 lbs. 2 oz. I'll never forget the moment RayAnn was brought to the hospital to meet her new brother. Her little-bitty, cute self walked in the hospital room, and we locked eyes. She ran up to me, and I hugged her tight. The emotion within me was overwhelming. I loved this baby boy with all of my being, but when RayAnn walked through those doors, I felt that same rush. I may not have birthed her, but I loved her just the same. She was my child.

One week after the birth of Presley, we got the news we had been hoping and praying for. RayAnn was legally ours. She was adopted on April 25, 2007. We had a large celebration party at our house and were joined by family, friends, neighbors, and teachers. The celebration of that day is one I will never forget. RayAnn had opened a piece of my heart that I didn't know existed. We rejoiced in the blessings we had been given and the life we never dared to dream for. It felt like we had been on the journey of a lifetime to get to this place. But as we were learning, God had other things in store for us. Our journey was really just beginning.

Chapter 3

Life, as it has a tendency to do, moved on. We settled in as an official family of four, and for a while, RayAnn continued to do well and make gains. Every once in a while, we would see some odd behavior in her. The symptoms were inconsistent and puzzling in both their variations and frequency. For example, she would go pale and start drooling one day, and then it wouldn't happen again for a while. She would fall asleep at odd hours—we would walk into her room and find her asleep on the floor in the middle of the day. At times her top lip would swell for no reason, and often we would notice that she had a "worried" look on her face, but it would pass just as quickly as it had appeared, and she would go back to being her usual self.

She was experiencing frequent falls, but at the time she was also a new walker (due to her cerebral palsy), so I didn't think too much of it. Then there would be times when she wouldn't respond when I was speaking to her, but again I didn't let it worry me. Occasionally the teachers at her school would mention that she had done something "funny" during the day but they couldn't put a finger on it either. It was never anything terribly obvious, but we knew *something* was going on. I would mention it to her neurologists, but they would always chalk it up as nothing to worry about or as being related to her cerebral palsy and would prescribe her more CP-related medicines to try and counteract what we were seeing. The episodes would last for only a few minutes—sometimes only a few seconds—and then they would pass; there were seemingly no other side effects of the behavior at the time, so we accepted what the doctors told us and moved on.

In truth, we weren't terribly concerned about the odd behaviors at the time because RayAnn was doing so well. She was attending a regular daycare, taking swim lessons, and going to ballet. She was potty-trained, which we had been told would be a huge feat for a child with her diagnosis. She was making amazing strides at her twice-a-week therapy appointments and doing great with her AFOs (another name for her leg braces). From that first day I met RayAnn, she had always had a feisty spirit and a can-do attitude. She never let anything slow her down. She didn't care if she fell down one time or twenty. She would always pick herself back up and refused help from anyone—she was determined to do it herself!

In 2008 I gave birth to my daughter, Gabrielle. Again, God had a plan for us, and Gabby was a huge part of it. With the birth of our precious daughter, we also received one of RayAnn's biggest blessings. Through the years Gabrielle has been an incredible sister, friend, and advocate for RayAnn.

I was a new mom to three kids—a five-year-old with special needs, a not-quite-two-year-old toddler, and now I had a newborn. RayAnn was experiencing a huge life transition as she started kindergarten and faced the challenges of the school day and dropping her nap. To say I was under a lot of stress at that point in my life is an understatement. I could see that this stress was taking a toll on RayAnn as well as we began to witness her seizure activity. She seemed tired all of the time and was having more bad days than good. I took careful notes and began to notice patterns in her seizure activity—any sort of stress, even if it was "good" stress, like Christmas excitement, could trigger a seizure in her. A lack of sleep could set her off as well, so I became obsessed with her sleep schedule and making sure she was getting to bed on time and keeping the house quiet so she could rest. If she was sick, particularly if she had a fever, it would almost always guarantee a seizure at some point.

In the beginning I frantically rushed her to the emergency room or the neurologist's office every time she had a seizure. I wanted answers: Why was she seizing again? What was causing it? What could we do to try and stop it? She was receiving her anti-seizure meds as prescribed, and we were doing everything the doctors instructed us to do, and yet, we weren't seeing any improvement. In fact, things were getting worse. I was never given an explanation, and, instead, the neurologist would add *more* medications or increase the doses of the existing medications. Her health began to deteriorate, and all of those gains we had worked so hard for started to slip away. It seemed as though we spent our entire lives either in the emergency room, for chipped teeth and stitches, or at the neurologist's office, for tests and medication adjustments, and still we weren't getting the answers we needed.

> It seemed as though we spent our entire lives either in the emergency room or at the neurologist's office, and still we weren't getting the answers we needed.

As these episodes continued, the symptoms we were seeing seemed to intensify and multiply. Suddenly, instead of just drooling, her eyes would begin to twitch, her right arm would curl up, and then she would go pale and take a nap. Or, if the seizures escalated, she would convulse, lose control of her bladder and bowel, vomit, and at times lose consciousness. She was starting to recognize when an episode was coming and would come to me, with that same worried look from before, but now she would point to her chest and want me to hold her. It was in the middle of one of these episodes that all at once, the light came on for me. The symptoms were becoming more textbook by the day—these odd behaviors we were witnessing *were* seizures. All this time when she would go pale and drool, she was seizing! Not one of her neurologists at that time had educated me on what non-typical seizure behaviors might look like. In fact, there are actually many different types of seizures that have varying symptoms depending on where they originate in the brain. Like so many other things in this journey, I'd had to figure it out for myself.

With this new realization in hand, I began working to try and figure out what was going on with her and how best to treat it. I spent hours online researching and reading everything I could get my hands on about epilepsy. But it seemed that no matter what we tried, we couldn't get control of the seizures—we never could get ahead of them. It was during this time that I *really* began to feel my way through this journey as a parent advocate for my chronically ill child. Oh, I had advocated for her all along—I had researched and gone to therapy appointments and countless doctors' appointments. I had dosed medicines and read about side effects and discussed care plans. But it was then that I started to find my strength and realized that the buck would have to stop with me when it came to getting RayAnn the right care *for her*.

It took me some time to figure it all out. I had to learn about RayAnn and *her* seizures. What were *her* triggers? What did *her* symptoms look like? What did increasing the doses on medications look like *for her*? I weighed everything the doctors were telling me to do against what I knew about my daughter and what was happening to her on a daily, hourly, and sometimes minute-to-minute basis. This is when I found my own voice and learned to tell these doctors (whom I both trusted and respected), "Wait a minute—no," when they suggested things that didn't feel right for us.

All of a sudden, it seemed as if RayAnn's seizures became out of control. One afternoon as RayAnn stepped off the school bus, I took one look at her and knew something wasn't right. She was pale and had a look in her eyes that I recognized instantly—she'd had a bad day and had been seizing. I took her to see her neurologist, desperate for something—anything—we could try to help her. I'll never forget that moment, as we stood in the exam room and I pleaded with him to admit her to the hospital, and he said, "You need to stop being her nurse and be her mom." That was the final straw for me. "No," I told him. "I'm taking her to the hospital. You can admit her or I will take her to the ER myself." He begrudgingly agreed to start the admission process, and we headed to the hospital. After we arrived and RayAnn was hooked up to the EEG, panic set in among her treatment team as they realized she was status epilepticus (SE is a life- threatening condition in which seizures follow one another without recovery of consciousness between them). They rushed her to the PICU and started pushing meds. Everything was moving so fast, and I was filled with terror. My worst fears were coming alive right before my eyes as I watched RayAnn's frail body convulse uncontrollably. I thought that was it for our beautiful baby girl.

My worst fears were coming alive right before my eyes. I thought that was it for our beautiful baby girl.

Peyton and I sat vigilant at her bedside, wracked with fear. RayAnn was on a ventilator in a medically induced coma. The visual of her, so small and frail, surrounded by the various tubes and monitors—and the terror I felt in that moment—is something that I will never forget. As a nurse, I was in a familiar setting, surrounded by equipment I was trained to operate. But as a mother, it all felt scary and new. I refused to leave her side and constantly monitored her for any signs of change or discomfort. I felt frantic and scared, and not at all like the calm and assuring nurse I had been trained to be. Finally, the doctors insisted we get some sleep that night so that we could be fresh for the procedures they wanted to try in the morning. They sent us to a nearby room to try to rest. In the middle of the night, I woke up in a panic. I knew something was wrong with my baby. I just knew it. I woke up Peyton but he told me to go back to sleep—he assured me that someone would come to wake us up if something was wrong with RayAnn. But I couldn't. I got up and went down the hall to RayAnn's room and found her lying in her bed with tiny tears rolling from her sleeping eyes and down her cheeks. I immediately started to cry and called the nurse. She told me that they had just catheterized RayAnn and she had been upset during the process and fussed a bit. What a moment that was for me as her mother! It was then that I knew, with all my heart, that you don't have to give birth to your child to have that special connection to them. I felt that something was wrong with her and I knew she was in pain. It woke me up from a dead sleep! This was the moment when I truly learned to listen to my gut intuition—to pay attention to that connection and that little voice telling me that as RayAnn's mother I knew what she needed. I learned then how to tap into that so that I could help her and advocate for her in the way she needed most.

This was the period of time in our lives that things really began to feel desperate. I felt like I was turned on all the time. Every minute of my day was spent making sure that she was safe. I was constantly watching her—even at night. Epilepsy patients are at risk for a condition known as SUDEP, or Sudden Unexpected Death in Epilepsy Patients. SUDEP is the unexpected death of a seemingly healthy person with epilepsy, where no cause of death can be found. Out of the nine main risk factors for SUDEP, RayAnn met seven. We set her bedroom up with multiple baby monitors. I became a tyrant about her sleep schedule to make sure she got enough rest, because lack of sleep was a seizure trigger for her. To say the least, life became very challenging as I tried to juggle my full-time job as a clinical research nurse along with my duties as a wife and mother to two other small children who also needed me as well. We tried countless medications and combinations. It seemed impossible at times to figure out which of the medicines were actually helping and which ones were possibly making her worse. RayAnn, our sweet seven-year-old girl, was getting worse by the day. Her hair was falling out, and she was pale with dark circles under her beautiful blue eyes. Her body was covered in bruises and scrapes from the constant falls her seizures caused. She was weak and was in a wheelchair or had to be carried everywhere. I felt helpless and frustrated.

Constantly on the search for more options, we went to Miami Children's Hospital, where RayAnn underwent testing to see if she was a candidate for epilepsy surgery. After the testing was complete, we were presented with three options. We could try a VNS, or a vagus nerve stimulator. Sometimes referred to as a "pacemaker for the brain," this is a device that is placed under the skin in the chest and has a wire that is connected to the vagus nerve, which is an important pathway to the brain. It emits a small, constant current with the hope that it would help to stabilize seizure activity in the brain. They also presented the option of a corpus callosotomy, which is an operation that cuts the corpus callosum in the brain, essentially severing the connection of the left and right brain in order to limit seizure activity from spreading between the two halves of the brain. And lastly, they offered for us to try another AED, or anti-epileptic drug, that was new on the market (and not FDA-approved for use in children at the time). Based on the options presented to us, we felt like the VNS was the best and most hopeful option for RayAnn. (Unbeknownst to us, the VNS was also not FDA-approved for use in children under the age of twelve. While it is now, it feels ironic to look back and remember this as it has become one of the biggest arguments against our current treatment regimen.) She had the VNS implanted, and we moved forward.

At this time, RayAnn was taking four different medications for her epilepsy and was being given the maximum dose for two of the four she was on, and yet she was still seizing. I was giving her Diastat (diazepam rectal gel) for seizures lasting longer than five minutes and was constantly paranoid about going anywhere or having RayAnn out of my sight for fear she would seize and we wouldn't have the emergency medication with us.

We were fortunate enough to have a "wish" granted for RayAnn by the Make-A-Wish Foundation, a non-profit organization that grants wishes to children with life-threatening medical conditions to renew strength and courage. RayAnn's wish was to meet princesses, so our family was granted a trip to Disney World to make this happen for her. She was so sick during this trip, but, typical RayAnn, she didn't want to miss a minute of the excitement and didn't let it hold her back. We tried to make every moment that she felt well count for something—make memories, spend time as a family, let RayAnn be out in the world to have new experiences. Those moments seemed few and far between—RayAnn was just so incredibly sick. We had also had enough time with the VNS at this point to feel like it wasn't really making a difference for her and we knew we needed to revisit our options.

It wasn't long before she went into status epilepticus again. We found ourselves back in the PICU with our sweet girl hooked to a ventilator and fighting for her life. It was at this point that we came face to face with our worst nightmare—our neurologist told us that we should begin preparing ourselves to say good-bye to our daughter. I don't know if I can ever accurately describe the way it felt—the gripping fear and sudden devastation. At the same time, I was overcome with anger and determination—I felt like our doctors were giving up on RayAnn and I wasn't going to do that. I refused to say good-bye and knew we would fight through this no matter what it might take. Our girl was a fighter, and by the grace of God she pulled through, and we were more determined than ever to find the solution that would save her life.

We decided it was time for a third opinion so we visited UF Health Shands Hospital. We specifically asked for the head of the program, Dr. Paul Carney. We had great hope that he could help us to find some answers. We stayed for a week, and RayAnn was hooked up to an EEG (a test used to evaluate the electrical activity in the brain) for constant monitoring of her seizure activity. Dr. Carney explained to us that he felt strongly that no one should be on four anti-epileptic drugs and still seizing. "Something is not right," I remember him saying to us, and I felt an immense relief at feeling that someone was finally listening to us and hearing our cry for help. He explained to us that he wanted to take RayAnn off of some of her anti-seizure meds to see how she would respond. I was terrified of what this might do to her but felt like we were running out of other options so I was willing to try anything. In two days, her EEG showed improvement in her seizure activity just from dropping one of the medications. I began to feel hope and also found myself opening up to a new world of possibilities. Until this time, I had been (willingly) following what the doctors had said to do—upping doses and trying new medicines and combinations. But this physician opened my eyes to the realm of possibilities when it came to RayAnn's treatment by proposing something completely unconventional—instead of adding *more* meds to her treatment plan, he wanted to find the right meds *for her* and get rid of the ones that weren't working. For six months RayAnn did really well on this new trial. It felt like we were seeing our RayAnn again. She wasn't having as many seizures—she was more alert and doing well at school. She was swimming again with her swim team and getting stronger and looking healthier. It was thrilling! However, after about six months, the medicine combination seemed to stop working, and she started to slowly slip back into her old symptoms again. But those six good months had lit a fire in me. I wanted that life for RayAnn and now I knew it was possible; I just had to figure out the *how*. I was determined to find a solution that would help us get her there.

To say we tried everything is an understatement. No matter how outside of the box or unusual it may have sounded, if it wasn't harmful to RayAnn, I was willing to give it a shot. We visited holistic healers, saw a chiropractor, and tried fish oil and many different specialized diets. Some of these therapies seemed to help, but we never saw any real success.

We were on a merry-go-round with no end in sight. RayAnn was growing, and as a result of her increased size, her falls were becoming harder and more damaging. The calls from school about seizures were increasing in frequency. I was living in a state of constant fear. Our marriage felt the strain of the constant stress, and our other children began to show signs of weariness from it as well. I was RayAnn's mother and I was the person who was supposed to be able to help her and to make things better and I couldn't. I had been in the hospital as a nurse and had seen all of these things before. I understood the terminology and the medical science behind the things the doctors were telling us to do. But being a mother facing all of these things with my own daughter was almost more than I could bear. Nothing we had tried was working, and it seemed as though we were out of options. I was devastated—but I was not giving up. And then, like everything else in this story of ours, we found our next path in the most unexpected of places: television.

I was devastated—but I was not giving up.

Peyton was watching television one day and happened to catch a documentary featuring Dr. Sanjay Gupta called *Weed*. And for the first time in what felt like ten lifetimes, we had a ray of hope again.

Chapter 4

My husband, Peyton, pulled me into the room where he had been watching a documentary on television. "You've got to see this," he said. As the images flashed across the screen, we couldn't believe it. We sat there, side by side, with our mouths hanging open. It seemed unbelievable to us—too good to be true! Could the solution we had been looking for be that simple? Could *cannabis* really be the answer?

The CNN documentary *Weed* followed well-known neurosurgeon and CNN medical correspondent Dr. Sanjay Gupta as he spent a year traveling the world and interviewing medical leaders, experts, growers, and patients in an effort to investigate medical marijuana. Initially he decided to do the documentary as a way to prove his point that medical marijuana was not a viable option for treating patients with true medical conditions. (Up to this point, he had been vocal in the media about this viewpoint and even penned an article for *TIME* magazine in 2009 titled "Why I Would Vote No on Pot.") After the completion of the documentary, he issued a public apology stating that he had been wrong. Once he met the families and patients featured in the film, he changed his mind and now saw that medical marijuana was a viable, useful treatment in the medical world for patients suffering a variety of ailments, including epilepsy. Of particular interest to us, however, was the portion of the documentary that told the story of Charlotte Figi, a little girl in Colorado who suffered from Dravet Syndrome that had caused her to have debilitating seizures from her infancy. We were captivated by her story, as it rang so true to our own—her family had tried every treatment and medicine that existed and had come to what they felt like was the end of the road for Charlotte. They were losing their little girl the same way we felt like we were losing ours. Her parents discovered a way to make an oil from a high-CBD /low THC cannabis plant that was bred by local growers, the Stanley brothers. Figuring they had little to lose at this point, they began dosing Charlotte with the CBD-rich oil and saw immediate results. Charlotte's seizures significantly decreased. She began to come back to life—walking, talking, eating, and even feeding herself. We were stunned by the results we were seeing on the television screen and we knew we had to take immediate action to see if this was the thing that we had been hoping for—the miracle that would save RayAnn!

We were captivated by her story, as it rang so true to our own... they were losing their little girl the same way we felt like we were losing ours.

Peyton immediately got on the phone and was able to get in touch with the Stanley brothers. The Stanley brothers are six brothers who own and operate a company in Colorado (where marijuana is legal) that grows hemp and cannabis plants. They had bred this particular plant for a cousin who was going through treatment for cancer and needed something for pain management. (It was jokingly dubbed "The Hippie's Disappointment" because it was so low in THC and therefore wasn't any good for getting "high.") Once Charlotte began to successfully treat her seizures with the oil from this plant, they began to produce the oil and sell it under the name "Charlotte's Web." Peyton told them about RayAnn and gave them the run-down of our story. They invited us to come to Colorado to see their operation and to meet the people they were working with. We wanted—*needed*—to go see this for ourselves. We needed to see with our own eyes that this was real.

We didn't waste any time getting to Colorado. While we were there, we met with Paige and Charlotte Figi as well as several other families who had traveled from all over the country (and the world!) just to have access to Charlotte's Web for a loved one in their family. Most of them were there for their own children, and at that time, most of the families we met were part of the epilepsy community. As we spoke to them all, we found that every family seemed to have the exact same story. Our story. They too had exhausted all other treatment options. Their children were also dying before their eyes, and they didn't know what else to do. Now these kids were coming off the seemingly endless list of pharmaceuticals they had been prescribed, and they were coming alive, some of them for the first time in their entire lives. As we met these children and listened to their stories, my heart began to fill with hope for RayAnn and what this could possibly mean for her.

Once we had seen what Colorado had to offer RayAnn, we began to explore our options, which included the very real possibility of our uprooting our lives in Florida and moving there. It was important to us that we do this the right way—in a state where it would be legal for us to possess and use the CBD oil. Medical cannabis was not legal in our home state of Florida, so we would have to move—I planned to move as soon as possible with RayAnn and then figure out how Peyton and our other two children could follow us later. The logistics would not be easy, but if this was the solution for RayAnn, I knew I would move heaven and earth if it meant saving our girl.

I knew I would move heaven and earth if it meant saving our girl.

Little did we know that at the same time, a few cities over from us, Representative Matt Gaetz was watching the same documentary we had seen, and he too felt led to take action. He too called the Stanley brothers and asked them what he could do to help. The Stanley brothers were able to connect us with Representative Gaetz, and we began working together to make change happen. How exciting it was to think that this could not only be a possible treatment for RayAnn but that it could potentially be available in our home state! That would mean we wouldn't have to uproot our lives and leave our family and friends, our home, and our jobs. We could stay close to the community of medical and personal support that knew RayAnn and had both treated her and supported us for years.

We jumped right in, ready to assist Representative Gaetz as he began laying the groundwork for this bill. He held a workshop for the bill and invited Joel Stanley (one of the six Stanley brothers), Peyton and me, Paige Figi (who is the mother of Charlotte, the little girl from the documentary), and several others who could share their stories. It was a very empowering experience to share our own story. Hearing the stories of other families from Florida who were also desperate for this treatment convinced me more than ever that we had to stay and fight for this bill. We had to advocate for the right to have access to this treatment in Florida, for us and for the countless others who needed it.

Things really started to take off from that moment. As God proved time and again in our journey, he had our plan under control. I had a running buddy at the time (she was actually my pacer for the half-marathon I had just completed) who also happened to be a lobbyist, and she offered to help us as we learned to navigate the often-confusing world of government and politics. A friend Peyton grew up with happened to work as a media consultant, and she reached out to us and offered to help in any way she could—free of charge. It seemed as though at every turn God was providing the guidance and support we needed to make this happen. We got a game plan together and started taking meeting after meeting with Florida senators and representatives where we shared our story. In each meeting, it was so encouraging as we would watch people's reactions and opinions about medical cannabis change right before our eyes. I'll never forget a meeting that we had with a conservative House member who was also a Baptist preacher. Our lobbyist shared with us that he probably wouldn't support this bill but she felt like he needed to hear our story. By the end of the meeting, and after hearing our story, he was praying with us and became one of our biggest advocates.

> ## It seemed as though at every turn God was providing the guidance and support we needed to make this happen.

We were at a time when things were starting to feel hopeful again and we felt excited about being a part of what we hoped would be a monumental and beneficial change for so many in our state. But it was also a scary time for us. We had put ourselves and our daughter out there for all to see. We had told our story, and it was no secret to anyone what we were trying to do. We received messages from people we didn't even know threatening us—saying that we were horrible parents and they would turn us into child protective services for what we were planning to do for our daughter. Fortunately for us, the people in our inner circle were very supportive. Even our friends who maybe weren't fully on board with the idea of cannabis were fully supportive of our family and of RayAnn.

Our hard work paid off, and God answered our prayers. Senate Bill 1030 passed the Senate floor with veto-proof majority. RayAnn was honored on the Senate floor and received a standing ovation for her bravery and advocacy. Later that day, after the bill had passed, we met the governor, and he promised RayAnn that he would sign the bill into a law. He followed through on that promise. On June 16, 2014, Governor Rick Scott signed the "Compassionate Medical Cannabis Act of 2014" into law, which meant that soon RayAnn would be able to have access to the treatment that we had fought so hard for. It would still take some time for the Florida Department of Health to write the rules and regulations for this new law, but this first big step had finally happened. It was a victory worth celebrating. We were finally on the path to the miracle for which we had prayed for so many years.

Chapter 5

The passing of the bill was *not* the happy ending to our story. In fact, some two years passed before patients had access to actual treatments in our state. The wheels of government turn slowly, and we waited for what felt like an eternity.

When the Compassionate Medical Cannabis Act was passed, a system called the Compassionate Use Registry was created by the Department of Health that would allow physicians to add patients to the registry so that dispensaries would have a comprehensive, official list to refer to when dispensing medication to patients. As part of the law, a pediatric patient requires that two physicians sign off on their treatment in order to be added to the registry and have access to medication. We knew that would be the case for RayAnn when we decided to pursue treatment for her, and that we would need a physician from a private practice to sign off for her because our neurologist was connected to the University of Florida and would not be able to since it was a conflict of interest for his job. During our fight to have the legislation passed, we met a pediatric epileptologist when he was invited to come and speak at a rule-making workshop we were involved with. We knew that he had knowledge about medical cannabis and had a positive outlook on it as a treatment option. We hoped that his perspective as a physician who had seen it work in patients and who believed in the science behind it would be a welcome addition to what we were trying to accomplish. We decided to take RayAnn to see him—we were preparing for when the product would be available and preparing for all of the "what-ifs" to come as we ventured into this new unknown—and we felt like he would be a great ally for us.

When you've worked with doctors both as a nurse and over the years as a parent advocate to a sick child, you learn pretty quickly that there are some doctors you'll click with and some you never will. In the space of a few moments inside our first appointment with this physician, I knew that this was going to be a great fit for RayAnn. He really took the time to listen to us and hear our story, and he just seemed to *get it.* He was a huge advocate for wanting to help us figure out RayAnn's underlying diagnosis so that we could truly find the right treatment for her. At that time he was also doing some work for a lab that did genetic testing, and he helped us to get RayAnn tested, purely as a favor. Thanks to his kind gesture, we finally, *finally* had an answer for our girl. We learned that a variant was identified in the KCNQ2 gene consistent with early infantile onset epilepsy. KCNQ2 is a gene involved in the proper functioning of a potassium channel in the brain. Abnormal changes, or mutations, in the gene are associated with seizures. KCNQ2-related epilepsies represent a spectrum of conditions from mild to severe.

I immediately began to read everything I could get my hands on about this diagnosis. I connected with the KCNQ2 Cure Alliance and the Jack Pribaz Foundation. I had so many questions, but, ultimately, I wanted to know what treatments were successful for this diagnosis. I learned that doctors were discovering different mutations in the KCNQ2, which contributes to a spectrum of clinical outcomes—some children have no seizures after the age of three and some have persistent seizures that do not respond to medication. I also learned that although there is no specific treatment, seizures may respond to sodium channel blockers, like Tegretol (which RayAnn had tried). I made contact with the Baylor College of Medicine and registered her for their clinical trial (they were performing a study to understand causes and aid diagnosis of epilepsy caused by changes, or variants, in KCNQ2 and KCNQ3). I spoke with a neurologist at Baylor and came away from our conversation feeling like RayAnn was out of options. There are seizure medications being studied that specifically target the KCNQ2 potassium channels, but they were not (and are not currently) available for us to try. It was time for us to try medical cannabis. We had fought so hard to have this as a legal option in Florida, and we had won—but we were stalled as we waited for the red tape and ever-so-slow wheel of government to turn. We had done our part, and while the clock ticked by on putting the fruits of our labor in action, RayAnn (and all the other children in Florida hoping for this treatment) continued to wait and suffer the effects of her illness with no relief.

It was at our second meeting with the pediatric epileptologist when he looked at our daughter and then looked at me and said, "Holley, what are you waiting for?" We were in a difficult time with RayAnn. She was going through puberty and experiencing an increase in her seizures. He reminded me that we had fought for this chance for so long and now it was a reality. But what if we got in trouble for moving forward now instead of continuing to wait? What about my husband, my other children, our life here? The doctor's words broke the silence in the room. "I think it's time that you give this a try," he said, and that was the little push of encouragement that I needed. He wrote us a recommendation for our first dosing, and we were on our way. I took the order home and talked it over with Peyton that night. We talked extensively over all of the possibilities. We had to weigh the risks to our family by starting this "early" against the benefits it would provide for RayAnn. Could we risk legal action for the sake of one child? The answer was yes. We had to. If you've ever been the parent to a sick child yourself, you know that you would do *anything* in your power to help them, and that's the choice we were facing. We made a game plan in case anything were to happen. We had contingencies in place. If we waited any longer for the politics to work themselves out, we could very literally be risking our daughter's chance for survival. Peyton made arrangements to order Charlotte's Web. It was really happening!

> ## If you've ever been the parent to a sick child yourself, you know that you would do *anything* in your power to help them, and that's the choice we were facing.

As excited as we were to start seeing improvement in RayAnn, we were equally as cautious as we began this new treatment. Before we even began, her doctors had decided to collect a baseline of data from her so we would have a reference point for any side effects that occurred during treatment (good or bad!) and also to monitor her overall health as we moved forward. RayAnn had an EEG and an MRI along with several labs, and we set a schedule to continue this regimen of testing every six months to monitor her progress. When she went in for the pre-data appointment, they had to turn off the VNS in her chest (because it was magnetic) in order to do the MRI. We spoke to her doctors and decided to try leaving it turned off for a week just to see if we could tell a difference in her seizure activity and whether or not it was actually making any difference for RayAnn. Her seizure activity remained mostly unchanged, and we did not see any drastic changes from her VNS being turned off (i.e., they didn't get worse). We asked her doctor if we could turn back on the feature that would allow me to give a burst of stimulation when the magnet is swiped over the generator, and they were able to do this so that RayAnn was no longer receiving regular pulses of electrical energy (but I still had the option to swipe the magnet and "rescue" her in the event of a seizure). All of the preliminaries were taken care of, and we were ready to give RayAnn her first dose of Charlotte's Web!

When you think about the milestone moments of your child's life—the things you might record in their baby book or commemorate with a photo for the family album—you don't often think about a first dose of medicine being included on that list. For us, the day we gave RayAnn her first dose of Charlotte's Web, or her "special medicine" as she called it, was a momentous occasion for the Moseley family. We all gathered around—Peyton, Presley, Gabby, and me—and cheered as she took the first dose. We videoed the moment just like we did when our babies took their first steps and said their first words. It meant so much to us. We hoped with all our hearts that it was the beginning of something big.

> We videoed the moment just like we did when our babies took their first steps and said their first words. We hoped with all our hearts that it was the beginning of something big.

When it came to dosing RayAnn, I decided to take things slow, even slower than the doctors were suggesting. I felt nervous and wanted to be extremely cautious so that we could pay close attention to how this new treatment was affecting RayAnn. I especially wanted to be tuned in to any negative side effects she might experience, if there were any. The typical protocol for dosing with CBD-rich oil called for us to increase the dosage once every three weeks, but we went even slower. Her first dose was 0.2 ml, which was barely anything. We continued to give RayAnn the two prescriptions she was already taking for her seizures while starting her on the Charlotte's Web. It would be a long time before we even attempted to wean her off of those.

Within a few days of RayAnn's starting the Charlotte's Web, we began to see a positive change in her. Family members and teachers began to make comments about her—commenting on how she "looked so good today," or how her gait was so much better, or how she hadn't fallen for several weeks. For years I was filled with a sense of dread when my phone would ring during the day. It was often RayAnn's school calling to tell me that something bad had happened, like a fall or a seizure, and she needed to be picked up. Now I was getting calls from her school to tell me how great she was doing. They were seeing a marked improvement in her, and her teachers were thrilled. Cannabidiol (CBD) is a neuro-protectant and antioxidant, and it was bringing RayAnn's whole body back into homeostasis (balance). Along with decreased seizures, we were seeing improvements in many other areas: She had more energy, her color improved, she was walking better, and her hand-eye coordination was improving drastically (for example, she was able to peel an entire carrot with a vegetable peeler—something she had worked on but could not do before). Peyton and I made the decision to not tell the school about the Charlotte's Web at first. We knew that RayAnn's teachers loved her and would likely be supportive of us, but we didn't want to put them in a tough position until we knew the medicine was a success for RayAnn.

It took about six months before we started seeing *big* progress in RayAnn (like going weeks or months without a seizure, for instance). She was still having seizures every once in a while, but they were always illness-related, like if she would spike a fever or get sick. Inside the medical cannabis community, you'll often hear it repeated that "it takes time to find the right product and the correct dose." I think a lot of families hear the success stories and are so eager to do something for their children—to relieve them of their suffering and see real and lasting results—that they feel tempted to maybe try a larger dose or increase the dosing on a faster timeline in order to speed up the results. And I get it. I really do. I have felt that same desperation and the impatience as a parent of a child who is suffering. Looking back, however, I am *so* grateful that we took the time we did to take things slowly, and I truly believe that the tremendous success we have seen is largely due in part to our willingness to be patient.

During this time our pediatric epileptologist made the decision to move to a medical cannabis-friendly state, which led us back to Dr. Carney, whom we loved, but who worked for the University (which made working with medical cannabis tricky). He was unable to order this medicine for RayAnn but he did agree to help us with her dosing schedule and also to assist us as we began weaning her off the other pharmaceuticals she was taking. As slowly as we took the addition of Charlotte's Web to her treatment regimen, we took the removal of the pharmaceutical drugs she was on at a snail's pace. (In fact, as I am writing this, she is *still* being very slowly weaned off some of them.) The ability to remove *any* of the high-powered pharmaceuticals she has taken for years (even if it means still taking them but in smaller doses) has always been a huge win for us. The fewer side effects from medicines she experiences, the more RayAnn can shine through. It is so much easier to fight against the issues created by her diagnosis when we aren't also having to fight against the side effects of the drugs she is using to help keep her stable!

We went the entire school year that year without really telling anyone at RayAnn's school about what we were doing, being cautious in an effort to protect RayAnn and her teachers until we knew for sure that this was something that we planned to continue long-term. That August, at the following year's classroom orientation, I spoke with the mother of a little boy in RayAnn's class who told me about her son's struggle with seizures and her frustration over the treatments not garnering any real results for him. It was that moment that broke the silence for me. I realized that in keeping our story quiet, I was unintentionally keeping this amazing resource from others we knew who could utilize it for their own success stories! I immediately told her about Charlotte's Web and gave her the details of what we were doing, along with the resources to get her connected with the right people so that she could pursue treatment for her son. With that out in the open, I nervously told RayAnn's teachers about what we had been doing. To my surprise, my "confession" was met with laughter! They all told me they knew something was going on—there was such a difference in RayAnn, after all, it was pretty hard to miss! They were all very supportive (which we never really doubted they would be), and it was a relief to feel like we could be open and share our good news with those who had supported us and especially had been such a huge support to RayAnn for so many years.

RayAnn has been seizure-free since October 18, 2016. On August 10, 2017, RayAnn's EEG showed no spikes or seizure activity. The doctors couldn't believe it. In reviewing her past EEGs as a comparison, they were able to share with us that this was the best her EEG has ever looked. For the first time (ever!) in her medical records, her seizures were listed as "controlled." The doctor's note states, "I discussed that I cannot write for CBD oil but it does appear to have benefited this pharmacoresistant epileptic encephalopathy patient."

She continues to make amazing academic gains at school. She is involved with the Miracle League and our church youth group, and she participates in the Special Olympics in both basketball and volleyball (which is pretty amazing when you consider she spent years struggling to walk without falling!). She is a full-fledged teenager who enjoys spending time with her friends and listening to her music at the highest possible volume. She has dreams for herself: to go to college and live in a dorm with a roommate, to be a teacher, to someday travel to Paris. She wants to be independent. The CBD-rich oil gave RayAnn the most precious gift—it gave her a future. And in turn it gave *us* the priceless gift of a future that included her. It is all our hopes and dreams for our family come true.

One of the most beautiful parts about our life with RayAnn now is how her personality and spirit have been allowed to shine in the absence of her seizures. She has always had a magnetic personality but now she truly radiates wherever she goes. She has a vibrant energy and a sense of self-worth that rivals that of most adults. She knows who she is and she's unapologetic about it—a confidence that I often envy and aspire to emulate. Nothing about her life up until now has been easy, but she has never let it make her a victim. In fact, she's used her experiences to empower herself; she has a sense of purpose and a desire to advocate for others. RayAnn was a gift to our family from the first day I met her. She has brought out a side of me I didn't know existed—she pulled me out of my shell and turned me into an advocate. She brings us so much joy; our family wouldn't be complete without the laughter and love she brings.

The CBD-rich oil gave RayAnn, gave *us*, the most precious gift— it gave us a future.

If you had asked me years ago where I thought I'd be at this point in my life, advocating for medical marijuana wouldn't have even been a blip on the radar to me. But that's the funny thing about life and God's plan for us. He knew all along this is where I was headed, and when I look back at my life now, I can see the markers along the way where He was preparing me for what was to come. There were trials and hardship on my path, but there was also more joy and love than I ever could have imagined for myself. I thank Him every day for that ordinary shift at work on an ordinary day and for the little blue-eyed girl who changed everything in her own extraordinary way.

Photos

December 21, 2005: The day we brought RayAnn home from the hospital. Note the crib she had lived in for the past two months!

RayAnn with her grandmothers, MiMi and Nonna, at Easter in 2006.

The day RayAnn met her baby brother, Presley. I will never forget the moment I saw her cute self walk into the hospital room. My heart exploded with love and happiness. My two babies were perfect!

*The best feelings are those that have
no words to describe them.*

*We are overjoyed to announce
the adoption of*

RayAnn Alma Moseley

*Please join us to celebrate
this joyous occasion*

Wednesday, April 25, at 5:30 p.m.

5310 Potosi Way

The finalization of a child's adoption marks the finish line of a marathon. When a court issues a decree of adoption, your relationship as parent and child is permanently and legally established.

On Wednesday, April 25, 2007, RayAnn officially became a Moseley. (She was mine the moment she came home; however, a weight was lifted when it became official.) Here is our "official" family with the Honorable Judge Goodman.

After spending days in the PICU at Sacred Heart Children's Hospital, Peyton was finally able to hold RayAnn. She had just been weaned off the ventilator, and we were trying to wake her up.

RayAnn was discharged from the hospital, and we boarded a private jet to Miami Children's Hospital to have her evaluated for seizure surgery. (She was not stable enough for regular airline travel.)

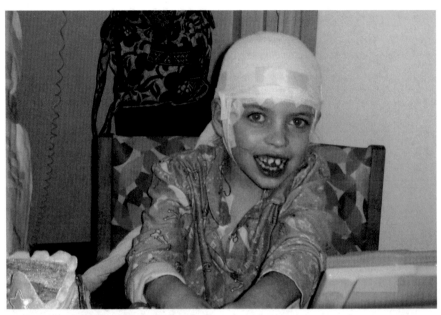

Make-A-Wish

We told RayAnn that she could have anything, and she chose to "meet the princesses." Even though she was not feeling well and having seizures, she was determined to not miss a moment of the fun! She got Belle, Cinderella, and Aurora all to herself for thirty minutes. It was magical!

This was a much-needed trip for our whole family.

Her only other "wish" would have been to meet Justin Bieber. RayAnn had Bieber fever!

Peyton and I visited Colorado and toured the greenhouse and lab where Charlotte's Web is grown and processed.

RayAnn's elementary class on March 26, celebrating Purple Day (an international grassroots effort dedicated to increasing awareness about epilepsy worldwide).

RayAnn was honored by Senator Rob Bradley on the Senate floor. She was given a standing ovation for her bravery and advocacy!

On May 13, 2014, Senate Bill 1030 passed! RayAnn had the privilege to meet Governor Rick Scott and sit in his chair. He promised her that he would sign the bill!

RayAnn was invited to meet Winter from the movie *Dolphin Tale!*

Winter serves as a symbol of courage, perseverance, and hope to millions of people—both able and disabled—who have been touched by her remarkable story of recovery and rehabilitation. Like Winter, we feel RayAnn serves as a symbol of strength, determination, and HOPE.

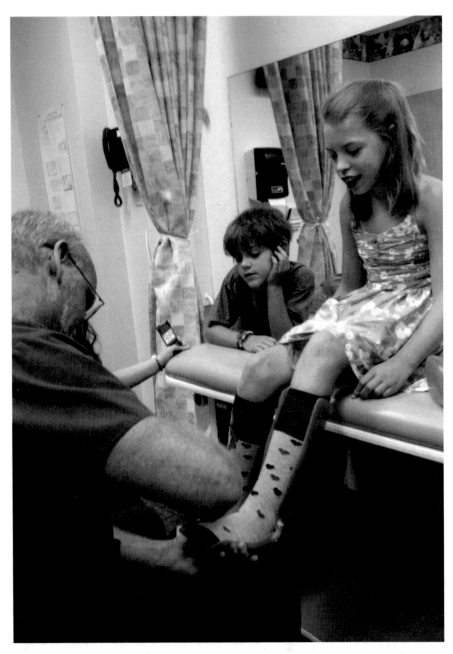

RayAnn is a patient at Shriners Hospital for Children in Tampa. They provide her orthopedic care. RayAnn wears bilateral AFOs on her legs. These work to prevent toe walking. She also had heel cord lengthening surgery at Shriners.

To celebrate the passing of the bill, RayAnn and Representative Matt Gaetz were invited to throw the first pitch at the Pensacola Blue Wahoos baseball game.

The Miracle League of Pensacola provides physically and mentally challenged children a safe place to hit, catch, and run on a baseball field. RayAnn has played with the Miracle League for several years. She enjoys spending time with her friends and is quite competitive with the game.

RayAnn is an athlete with Special Olympics. She has enjoyed playing basketball and volleyball while making new friends.

RayAnn and I were invited to share our story at the Kids, Veterans & Athletes: Connecting Through Cannabis press conference on Capitol Hill.

We shared RayAnn's success with CBD-rich oil and urged Congress to change the laws to allow for patient access and more research.

We also had a great time seeing the sights in D.C.!

What I want you to know about me!

By: RayAnn Moseley

My name is RayAnn Alma Moseley. I was named after my great grandmother Alma Heller.

I am 15 years old, and I just have to say that being a teenager is hard.

I love my family, even though my sister is bossy and my little brother can be a pest. :)

My favorite food is spaghetti and meatballs. My mom makes it for my birthday dinner every year.

I am not a girly-girl. I like to play and get dirty. However, I am all for GIRL POWER.

I like going to school. My teachers and friends are the best. Guess what? I like doing my homework as well.

I have cerebral palsy and may talk and walk differently from other kids. If you can't understand me, it's okay; I will gesture to help.

I have epilepsy but I don't let it define me. I like to do the same things as my peers. Don't be afraid to ask me questions about my condition.

I like to ride my trike around our neighborhood. I also enjoy playing board games. But beware—I like to WIN!

I participate in Special Olympics and Miracle League (baseball). I like being part of a team and spending time with my friends.

My favorite president is Abraham Lincoln, because he believed that everyone is created equal. While in Washington, D.C., with my mom, we visited the Lincoln Memorial and Ford's Theatre. It was so much fun!

I love to laugh and to watch funny movies. Some people say that laughing is the best medicine. I agree!

I am sarcastic. I get that from my dad. I love to joke around with people. I believe that you should not take yourself too seriously.

I am not shy. I like to meet new people and make new friends. Everywhere we go, we usually run into someone I know. When we are out and I see a friend, I will run up and greet them with a hug!

My mom and I are advocates for epilepsy and my "special medicine." Even though I am not fond of the taste, I know that it has helped make my seizures go away. I want other kids like me to be able to use it.

I don't like going to physical therapy. My mom says I have to go to stretch and get stronger. I could do without it. However, I go.

I go to church just about every Sunday. I like to help teach Sunday school to the younger kids. I am also part of the youth group at church. We hang out, do volunteer projects, and study the Bible.

I say my prayers every night before bed.

I know my strengths and my weaknesses. I may not run fast, but I am confident in who I am. I will take up for myself and others. Bullies don't scare me. I am RayAnn Moseley!!!!!!

Part 2

Chapter 6

The Starting Line

Parents of medically fragile children are no stranger to the feeling of being overwhelmed. We are constantly faced with ever-changing treatment protocols, prescriptions and dosing, and research that continuously evolves. Our lives are unpredictable, at best. Often the thought of trying something new and different can feel like an insurmountable obstacle, even when it is something you are excited for. The questions and what-ifs can seem endless. What does the research say? How do I know what dosing should look like? Where can I find a doctor who will help us? The work that needs to be done *before* you even start can feel like a marathon.

Like most things in life, the hardest part of undertaking any-thing new is always getting started. Incorporating medical cannabis into your child's wellness routine is no exception. And of course, when you desperately *need* a health solution that works, trying something new and unfamiliar can seem all the more daunting. How can you even know where to begin? My best advice is this: Start with what you *do* know and take things one day at a time. Each new experience will give you more information and make the path ahead a little clearer.

Before we decided to go down this path with RayAnn, we felt we were quickly running out of options for her. I had already read all the books I could get my hands on and scoured the websites for anything that might help our daughter. We had explored virtually every pos-sible avenue at our disposal and it felt overwhelming to move into a new world of unknowns. However, this time I had a renewed sense of hope that helped to propel me forward. This was the first time I felt something might actually work. I felt prepared and knew the side effects were minimum to none, but I knew we would likely face a lot of roadblocks due to legal issues, and that was an entirely new fight for us to take on.

As we discovered during our experience, patience pays off in the long run. Being careful and diligent on the front end will truly pay off over time. If you are a parent to a medically fragile child, you already know all too well that no two children and no two cases are alike. As a nurse, I always approach each patient with a fresh set of eyes and ears, because what has worked well for one child may not work as well for another. It's crucial that you keep this in mind as you approach any new treatment option with your own child.

It is my hope that these tips will help to give you a basic check-list to get you started—a roadmap, if you will. If you ever feel overwhelmed, refer back to this list and choose one item to tackle head-on before moving to the next one.

Getting Started: At-a-Glance

- Find a state where medical cannabis is legal.
- Find a doctor who will work with you and help guide you.
- Apply for a medical marijuana card.
- Find a safe, quality product.
- Budget!

How to Seek Treatment

First, find a state where cannabis is legal. The first step in starting treatment is figuring out *where* it is available. Unfortunately, cannabis may not be legal in the state where you currently live. It was illegal in Florida until the Compassionate Medical Cannabis Act was signed in 2014. In fact, when we initially decided to pursue this course of action for RayAnn, we considered traveling to Colorado to seek legal treatment. When considering where you are going to seek treatment (and potentially move), it is so important to research every aspect thoroughly. You should choose a state where your condition is covered and that also has a quality version of the product you need. Certain states also have parameters on THC, so be sure to look into this in any place you consider. Each state has different laws and those laws are constantly changing, so doing your research and staying up to date are key!

Check with your doctor. I can't stress enough the importance of having a doctor involved in this process with you from the very beginning. Once you've decided the *where* and start the process of your *how*, you should secure a physician you trust, who is both qualified and willing to work with you on this treatment method. You should start by checking with your current physician to see if they will assist you with ordering medical cannabis. If your physician is unable (or unwilling) to assist you, then you need to begin looking for a physician who can help. Some states require that the physician take and pass a course before they are allowed to do so (for example, this is the case in Florida). You should also keep in mind that some states require that two different physicians sign off for a pediatric patient, so you'll need two doctors who will work with you. This is the most important step of this entire process and the one I believe you should square away before you do anything else.

Reach out to others who use or have used medical cannabis. Try to connect with other parents or adults who have experience with medical cannabis for useful information. They may have valuable insight from their own experiences. Ask them which doctors and dispensaries they recommend, and why. You may be able to find message boards or support groups online to pass on great tips to make your journey easier. This can be a powerful asset for you, but I also want to caution you here. You may run into people online who will try to give you medical advice (like what dosage to give your child) based on their own experiences. While it's okay to consider someone else's experience, do not take the advice of someone online over that of the physicians who are treating your child. You can never be too careful, and what may work for one person won't always work for another.

And besides, no person online can have your child's complete medical history to consider when giving out advice.

Figure out a game plan for access. In most states, getting access to medical marijuana requires a medical marijuana ID card. You may be surprised to find that acquiring a card can be a lengthy and sometimes complicated process. And even once you have completed the necessary steps, it can still take some time for your state's medical marijuana office to complete the process. For example, these are the steps to treatment in Florida:

1. Patients must first be diagnosed with a qualifying medical condition by a qualified ordering physician.

2. Patients and their caregivers will then be entered into the Medical Marijuana Use Registry by their qualified physician.

3. Patients and their caregivers will then apply for their registry identification card, which includes:

   a. An approved passport-type photo

   b. Proof of residency

   c. Application fee

While the exact requirements may not be the same in every state, having an idea of what to expect before you begin the process can be a huge help as you gather necessary documents and find physicians.

How to Choose the Right Product

Do your homework!

It is important for you to educate yourself on the endocannabinoid system. Here are some important facts to get you started:

- The endocannabinoid system (or ECS) is a biological system composed of endocannabinoids and cannabinoid receptors that are expressed throughout the entire body: the brain, organs, connective tissues, glands, and immune cells.

- Human and animal bodies make endocannabinoids naturally.

- Endocannabinoids help maintain optimal balance in the body, also known as homeostasis (possibly the single-most important system within our entire bodies).

Read reviews for user experience insights. For honest feedback on specific cannabis brands, check out reviews by real users online. You can ask your doctor for resources or consult with other families in your area.

Contact the medical cannabis company nearby for useful info. Try calling a few medical cannabis companies or dispensaries and ask questions about the products they offer. For instance, you might ask which formulas are known to be successful with your specific diagnosis. A good dispensary will be both knowledgeable and transparent. If you find one that isn't, move on.

Select a product with detailed labels. Look for clear labels that indicate the strain name, strain type, and total number of cannabinoids present. Be sure the brand you choose offers a batch number, who manufactured the product, and expiration date.

Pay attention to quality. Stay away from ingredients like artificial additives, preservatives, corn syrup, trans fats, or GMOs.

Aim for tested and proven products. It's important to realize that the quality of the cannabis product can vary depending on the conditions under which it was grown. Try to find and purchase a product that has been tested. Look for "lab tested" on the label. You also want a product that is free of pesticides, harmful bacteria, mold, and residual solvents. It is also good to look for a product that has had third-party lab tests done (many states require this, but you should look for it nonetheless).

Take careful notes. Be sure you always know what products your child is currently using and what they have used in the past. Include the strain, the dosage amount and times it is given, and the effect on your child. Also, be sure to list any side effects they experience. Choose a notebook that is small enough to carry with you; that way you can record any symptom the moment it occurs. Be sure to keep a writing utensil (or three!) handy as well. It also doesn't hurt to transcribe your notes digitally, so you'll have a record in case something happens to your notebook, or so you can easily email copies to your spouse, other caregivers, or different members of your medical team. If you're more technologically inclined, you can download a notetaking app onto your smartphone (which we never leave home without!) to record notes in the moment and then write down or download to one common place when you are home.

Stay organized with a binder or file folder. Along the journey to find solutions for your medically fragile child, you will collect lots of important information. Keeping a binder or file folder can help you stay prepared for doctor's visits and keep your notes all in one place. I keep RayAnn's important medical documents in a binder. I have tabs for: genetic testing, neurology, orthopedic, immunizations, IEP, etc.

Money Talk

As a parent to a medically fragile child, you are likely no stranger to bills, the reality of the cost of care, and prescriptions with price tags that look more like a car payment. The difference with medical cannabis is that you already know going in that you can't depend on insurance coverage.

Expect a hefty price tag. Medical cannabis products can cost anywhere from hundreds to thousands of dollars a month, depending on the dispensary, the product, and the required dosage. And because insurance doesn't cover medical cannabis, you'll have to pay for it out of pocket. In this case, I like the motto "Expect the worst but hope for the best." If you plan ahead of time for a hefty price tag and in the end it costs less, you'll just end up being overprepared—which is never a negative thing when it comes to finances!

Start saving money ahead of time. When you begin your initial research, start setting aside money to cover the cost of the treatments. It can take time to get to the point of actually having a prescription in hand and heading to a dispensary. Use this time to be as prepared as possible. Treat this fund like a health savings account. That way, once you settle on a dosing regimen, you'll have a better idea of what your month-to-month costs will be. Remember: It never hurts to go into a new situation overly prepared.

Above all, remember that when moving into uncharted territory, it is very normal to feel overwhelmed. As a parent on the proverbial "other side" of this starting-out process, I want to encourage you to take it slow. I can't stress enough how patience will pay off in the long run. If you take things one day at a time and stay vigilant, you will eventually see the results you are hoping for and make real progress that benefits your child.

Chapter 7

How to Build the Best Team for Your Child

Have you ever heard the old adage "It takes a village" when it comes to raising children? It's true! As parents, we learn pretty quickly that no matter how capable or qualified we are, we can't raise our little ones to be healthy, successful adults alone. It takes a conglomeration of people to help us get our kids to the "finish line" of adulthood—everyone from our family and neighbors to mentors and teachers, coaches, and friends play a key role in helping to shape and mold our children. (And let's be honest—they help to keep us sane along the way!) When you're the parent to a chronically ill child, that "village" is truly a life saver. As we've already discussed, caring for a sick child can be a very daunting and lonely job. Even though you are glad to do it, you bear the weight of a responsibility that never ends, and all the doubt and fear that go along with it. And for most of us, we are parents—not doctors or medical experts. This is why having a solid support team in place is such an important lifeline; it offers you backup and reminds you that you aren't alone. But getting such a team in place doesn't happen overnight.

A team is defined as a number of persons associated in joint action—working toward a common goal. When it comes to forming your own support system, it's crucial that you keep this in mind—the common goal is the health of your child, and they should be there to support you every step of the way. It took time, effort, and patience to create a team that could support RayAnn, as it will take time for you to find the right doctors, build trusting relationships, and piece together a plan that improves your child's quality of life and helps them thrive. The following tips will help you build a strong, compassionate, and capable team to advocate and care for your child.

First, know that *you*, the parent, are the team leader. First and foremost, understand that the patient and their parents should be the most important people on your medical team. The reason is this: You know your child better than anyone. You understand their quirks and have insight into what is working and what isn't working in their protocol. Further, no one else can or will advocate for your child better than you. You know their medical history and what other doctors or specialists have said or recommended in the past. Your doctors and specialists are certainly important as well, but they see your child for only a short time during their appointments. So be empowered by the fact that you truly know your child the best. Therefore, it is your job to head up the team.

Educate yourself as much as possible. As the leader of your child's care team, it is up to you to be as knowledgeable as possible about your child's condition and the treatments available. Following your gut is an important part of the caring for your child, but remember that you need to have an "educated gut." This means doing the work of researching your child's health condition and learning all you can about their diagnosis. Your knowledge, combined with your gut intuition, gives you the resources you need to be a strong member of your child's team.

When my children were young, we often took trips to Barnes & Noble so I could research epilepsy while the children played in the kids' area. There, I would read everything I could find about epilepsy. I particularly enjoyed the books written by people who actually *had* epilepsy, because they offered such a different perspective from the books I had read that were written by medical professionals. Overall, I know that this "education" I received helped me be a better advocate for my child.

Start with a good foundation. You may need to build your team of medical professionals from the ground up, so it's important to start off with a solid foundation. Priority number one on that list is finding a good pediatrician, and then finding a specialist, depending on your diagnosis. For RayAnn, we began by working with a pediatrician our family knew well and trusted completely. If you are in a small town and don't have many options for finding a specialist for the care you need—such as a university or research hospital—you may need to consider looking elsewhere for these initial resources.

Look for a doctor you can trust (and don't stop until you find one). Caring for a medically fragile child can be a terrifying experience in which you constantly fear for their well-being. It's important that you choose a doctor who supports and uplifts you and your child, rather than one who piles more fears and negativity onto your already-full plate. That said, you should feel good about the doctor you ultimately choose to care for your child. A good doctor should make you feel listened to and respected, and will let you know that they are working with you. You should leave appointments feeling encouraged and well equipped to move forward—not hopeless or defeated. Before you try out a new doctor, see if you can find some of their patients and get their opinion. Word of mouth is a great way to find great physicians and avoid those who may not be a good fit.

And speaking of less-than-ideal doctors, it's perfectly okay to decide that a certain doctor isn't a good fit for your child. Don't be afraid to try others or get a second opinion—or a third, or a fourth! In fact, your doctor should *encourage* you to get second opinions! The point is, keep looking until you find the doctor who gives you hope. You'll feel a tremendous peace in leaving a doctor who only adds to your fear for another one who gives you the hope you need. (And remember, just because you try out other doctors doesn't mean you can't go back later on.)

It may take some time to find a doctor who is open to treating your child with medical cannabis. Use social media sites like Facebook to connect with other families and get their recommendations for doctors who have experience treating patients with medical cannabis. In the meantime, your current doctor can still be a valuable resource; they can monitor your child for drug interactions and order necessary diagnostic tests and bloodwork as you continue your search.

Don't give up when you hear "no." Because RayAnn's treatments were covered by Medicaid, we were given a list of doctors and told that they were our only options. But on many separate occasions, I fought to get appointments with doctors outside of that list. At one point, when we asked to see a different doctor, RayAnn's case worker gave us a definitive "no." However, I was able to find and contact a supervisor willing to work with us. We submitted the necessary paperwork, and sure enough, RayAnn was approved to visit our preferred doctor instead. The lesson here is to be prepared to fight for what you want and need. Don't always accept the first answer you are given if it isn't the answer you are looking for. If you really fight for the care you know your child needs, you are much more likely to get it!

Don't be afraid to push back when something isn't working. As parents, it is also your job to determine whether something may or may not work for your family. One of our doctors recommended we try putting RayAnn on a ketogenic diet, but after trying a modified version, we didn't see any results and I knew that realistically it would be very difficult for our family to sustain that strict of a diet with two small children in the household. We returned to the doctor and asked for other recommendations to try.

Prepare for doctor appointments ahead of time. There's plenty you can do to get the most from your child's doctor appointments before you arrive. In fact, doing the right prep work is key to getting the most from your appointments. Prior to the visit, grab your journal or notepad and jot down any notes or questions you have. Make sure you also have a record of your child's medications, diagnoses, and symptoms, along with specific issues you want to talk about during the appointment. And remember that, ultimately, you are seeking a partnership with this medical professional, so showing up prepared is a great way to behave like a partner from the onset. And if you're seeing a doctor for the first time, it's a good idea to research them beforehand, so you know a little about them from the beginning.

Bring notes and take notes. It's wise to always bring your notes with you to doctor appointments. Your child's doctor has only so many minutes with you, so having organized notes ready helps you maximize your time with them. Be sure that you also take diligent notes while you're in the appointment as well. Some doctors will even print out information that you can take home and read over on your own. (If they don't offer, ask!) If notetaking isn't an option for you (because you have small children with you, for example), bring along another adult to take notes for you, ask questions you may have forgotten, and be a second set of ears to help you retain anything that was discussed during the appointment.

Always be working toward an integrated approach. With a chronically ill child, you will most likely see more than one type of doctor or specialist. So look for doctors who are willing to work together. Finding a team willing to consult with and work with one another is key, and you will find that many healthcare professionals are willing to comply. Trust me; it's far easier when you choose a pediatrician who will work with your neurologist, who will talk to your chiropractor, and so on.

Learn when to call on help (and when not to). You will likely need a doctor who is willing to work with your child outside of regular office hours or when emergencies arrive. But it's important that you learn what truly constitutes an emergency (and what does not), so that you don't abuse this privilege. In the beginning, it seemed like I took RayAnn to the emergency room for everything, but I figured out pretty quickly what was actually an emergency and what could wait until regular hours. Along our journey, several doctors gave me their cell phone numbers in case we ever needed their assistance at nights or on weekends, and I was careful never to use them unless there was a true emergency requiring their attention. After all, you need to keep the relationship healthy and respect the fact that your physicians have their own families and lives outside of their work. This will come with time and experience, but it is also a good idea to keep this in mind as you build new relationships with your team.

Select a team of caretakers you feel comfortable working with. (It makes a world of difference!) From doctors to teachers to childcare providers to in-home caregivers, your care team should consist of people you trust and feel comfortable working with. One of RayAnn's teachers went the extra mile to work with us so I could continue working while she was in school. Whenever RayAnn had a seizure, this teacher would call and keep us updated, but she really managed these situations herself. We were incredibly lucky that thanks to this teacher, we were not called to come pick up RayAnn early every day. We trusted this teacher's opinion and knew she would let us know if an urgent situation happened to arise.

Don't forget to include other kids on the team. It's very important for your child to have a community that helps them exist and function as normally as possible on a daily basis. Your child's peers can help tremendously in this regard. Whenever RayAnn started a new school year, I would go into the general ed classroom to introduce her to the other students. I talked about her diagnosis and answered any questions they had. This meeting engaged the children, helped them understand why RayAnn might seem a little different, and prepared them to support her in the classroom. It worked, and the students embraced her with empathy and were eager to learn and help out their new classmate. They even wore purple to support RayAnn on March 26, Epilepsy Awareness Day (Purple Day). It just goes to show you that other children can be compassionate allies for your child.

Expect to butt heads with someone on your child's team. It's likely that you won't always get along with every person on your child's team. But what's crucial is how you handle these situations. When disagreements or conflicts arise, it's best to face them head-on, instead of allowing them to fester and become worse. The sooner you tackle any differences, the better off you all will be. Keep things in perspective by remembering that your child's care is more important than anyone's temporary discomfort or hurt feelings! Also keep in mind that the person with whom you disagree also has your child's best interest at heart—just in their own way.

Find someone to support *you* too. As a parent, it's vitally important that you have at least one person to lean on as you fight for your child's well-being. You've got a difficult and at times scary job, and you may need someone to cry to, vent to, or just meet up with for a cup of coffee and a chat. This person could be your spouse, a friend, a neighbor, or a family member. Just make sure you have someone nearby to give you the support you need in those moments when you feel overwhelmed.

As you continue building your team, you will eventually start to see an incredible theme emerging: People really do care and want to help your child become as healthy and happy as possible. There may be times when you feel wracked by confusion, doubt, and uncertainty (in fact, you can probably count it!) but know that if you look for them, you will find helpers ready to assist you along the way. When doctors, friends, family members, caretakers, and teachers all work together, they can both support you *and* help your child make tremendous progress along the road to better health. Have trust in the process—your village is out there!

Chapter 8

Adventures in Trial and Error

If there's one thing I know for sure, it's that life is a game of trial and error. If you or someone you love has a chronic illness, you are probably used to the idea of trial and error more than anybody. And when it comes to treating epilepsy, in particular, trial and error is how doctors and patients figure out the right medications and doses that will work. For instance, you might hear your doctor say, "This medicine hasn't been tested or approved on a patient with *partial* seizures, but let's give it a try." Or you may hear something similar to, "This drug isn't FDA-approved for children, but I think we should try it." (This is known as off-label use, which has become a very common practice in the medical community; in fact, virtually every drug or device has been used off-label in some circumstance.) In short, we are no strangers to the game of trial and error or off-label use when it came to trying new treatments for RayAnn. (So you can see why giving something like medical cannabis a try was not a long shot for us—we had plenty of experience with treatments that weren't "approved"!)

Using cannabis as a medicine is also 100 percent a game of trial and error—especially until the federal government changes the policies and regulations to allow for more research on the health benefits of cannabis products. But trial and error is a different approach to treatment than most people may be used to—it's not exactly a "take two pills and call it a day" kind of game plan. But don't worry; you'll be fine if you follow a few simple steps. As a "seasoned veteran" of this method, I hope that I can bring some insight from my own experiences to help you as you are beginning a journey that may seem quite scary and overwhelming at first. I have always found that if you have a good foundation to start with, the rest of the task can hopefully feel a little less daunting. Keep the following guidelines in mind as you figure out what works for your child—and what doesn't work—and settle into your family's "new normal."

Make sure you start out with the right diagnosis. Understanding exactly what medical condition(s) you are dealing with is vital to knowing what treatment options are right for your child. Likewise, having a specific understanding of the exact diagnosis you are working to treat will help when you start the trial-and-error process of using medical cannabis.

Looking back, I realize there were several medicines RayAnn was on over the years that I wish we had avoided. In hindsight, it's clear that they were just wrong for her. It took a lot of trial and error for us to understand RayAnn and her seizure types, assess how she was responding to a new medication, decide whether it was a good fit or not, and, finally, choose to move on to try something new when it was clear something wasn't working. Through this whole process, we had to strike a delicate balance between RayAnn's seizures and the side effects from her medication. When we received RayAnn's genetic testing results of KCNQ2, it painted a clearer picture for us. We learned which anti-seizure meds were recommended and which were contra-indicated. The better we were able to understand her diagnosis, the clearer the treatment options became to us.

Be sure to work with a good physician… I cannot stress enough the importance of working with a physician when figuring out your child's treatment! Consulting with a doctor is crucial to your child's safety and well-being as you navigate uncharted territory together. Your doctor is also key in figuring out the correct dosing (which, again, will be a process of trial and error). They can provide a schedule on how to dose and slowly increase the dose until the desired outcome is reached—a common practice with any new medicine.

If part of your treatment involves weaning your child off of a current prescription, you must do so only under the instruction and careful guidance of your physician! Do not use the advice you find online or in a support group as guidance for weaning off medications, and do not, under any circumstances, "just wing it."

If you happen to live in an area where medical cannabis use is not common or live in an area where medical cannabis is newly legal (like it is in Florida), know you may have to look to other places to find a knowledgeable doctor able to help you. We found a great doctor in California, Dr. Bonni Goldstein, who had a lot of experience working with medical cannabis. We worked with her and got a lot of great help and advice. I highly recommend her book, *Cannabis Revealed: How the World's Most Misunderstood Plant Is Healing Everything from Chronic Pain to Epilepsy*, which breaks cannabis treatments down by the diagnosis.

... *and* **also work with a trusted medical cannabis company or dispensary.** Because some doctors may not be very knowledgeable about medical cannabis, make sure you are also working with a knowledgeable dispensary. An integrated approach is best at all stages of your treatment, so ideally your dispensary should be willing to work with your doctor and vice versa.

Your dispensary of choice should be one that guarantees you will have the product you need in stock when you need it. For example, when an epilepsy patient is weaned off of their previous anti-seizure medications, they depend heavily on the dispensary for the treatment that keeps them seizure-free. If the dispensary were suddenly out of their treatment, it would be disastrous for the patient.

Figure out which method of medical cannabis is best for your child. Everybody's body responds differently to the various types of cannabis and the different delivery methods. Choosing the right delivery method of medical cannabis comes down to your diagnosis and what symptoms you are trying to treat. Some points to consider:

- What effects are you looking for?
- How quickly do you need relief?
- How long do you want the effects to last?

There are many different types of delivery methods to choose from. They include vaporizing, smoking, edibles, tinctures, sprays, capsules, topicals, and transdermal patches. It can be quite overwhelming with so many choices. Talk with your physician to discuss which method may be best for you. A lot of patients may end up using multiple products to treat different symptoms.

Exactness of dosing may also affect the delivery method that you chose. For example, a cancer patient using medical cannabis for nausea treatment doesn't necessarily need their dose to be exact. But for an epilepsy patient like RayAnn, the dosing must be very exact. RayAnn uses a tincture, which is a liquid taken under the tongue for fast sublingual absorption and is sweetened for an overall better taste. By selecting this delivery method, I am able to measure and control her dose.

> Always treat medical cannabis like you would treat medicine. It should be handled and taken with care. Do plenty of research and ask questions of your medical cannabis company or dispensary, just like you would when picking up a prescription medicine at the pharmacy.

Do your research to make sure the product is safe and consistent. You can never be too careful when adding something new to your child's treatment regimen, so do your research! RayAnn takes Charlotte's Web, which is a whole-plant phytocannabinoid hemp oil extract. (It is *not* made from hemp seeds, like something you may find in the grocery store.) Charlotte's Web is organically grown in the United States and bottled in an FDA-approved facility. Some questions you may consider asking about the product you are purchasing:

- Where is the cannabis grown and processed?
- Has the product been tested for molds, mildews, and pesticides?
- Are batch results available?

Your products should deliver the same amount of cannabinoids in every package. For dosing, it is crucial to know that you are getting the same strength from month to month so your treatment can be effective.

"Start low. Titrate slow." As a general rule, it's best to start with a low dose and increase your child's dosage very slowly. Each time you begin a new dosage, be observant; make sure you aren't seeing any negative side effects, and that you are seeing at least some positive results. It's crucial not to rush through the process just because you're eager to see outcomes. Focus on taking things one step at a time, managing your expectations, and being patient throughout the process.

Remember that every experience is unique. Because no two bodies are exactly the same, each patient will react to their treatment in different ways. Age, diet, diagnosis, stress levels, and overall tolerance are just a few factors that make up your reaction to medical cannabis. In some cases, being male or female can even make a difference in which dose is right for you and how you will react to it. This is why it is crucial to pay close attention to the reactions or side effects the patient is having. Also be aware of possible drug interactions, particularly medications that are changed or broken down by the liver. Medical cannabis might increase the effects and side effects of some medications. Be cautious! And again, talk with your physician. Don't forget to take diligent notes to keep track of reactions! Even if a reaction seems insignificant, write it down. Include the time of day, what foods have been eaten, and what the temperature is that day. This level of diligence will make your treatment so much more successful in the long run.

Be wary of taking advice from others (no matter how well-meaning). Because traditional prescription medications undergo FDA testing for safety and efficacy, how the drug will be given to patients and at what dosage are known. But since scientific research of medical cannabis has been restricted in the U.S., and until we are allowed to study it further, there is no adequate way for patients to determine their appropriate dosage or method of ingestion. As a result, you may be tempted to turn to resources online for dosing advice. Don't do it! While it is okay to talk to others about their experiences, or seek recommendations for doctors on Facebook or other websites, never take dosing advice from anyone besides your doctor. Again, treat medical cannabis just like any other medicine; take only your physician's advice when it comes to dosing or adjusting this or any other medications your child may be on.

Even though there isn't as much research and information out there on medical cannabis as there is for other drugs and treatments on the market, it is starting to happen and will continue happening. It will come in time! So much has changed in just the last few years—there's so much more information now than when we first started this journey with RayAnn. Your trial-and-error phase to find answers and treatments that work should mirror the same steps you've already been taking to get you this far: do the research, work with your doctor, keep great records, be patient, and never, ever give up. Be the best advocate for your child that you can be. Trust me, it's the people who take the time to do their homework and stay diligent who reach success.

Chapter 9

Dealing with the Outside World:

How to Talk with Others about Medical Cannabis (and How to Handle Pushback)

Let's face it—as a parent to a sick child, you are likely no stranger to talking with other people about your child's health. Depending on the diagnosis, you likely field questions from casual acquaintances to well-meaning strangers to curious children every day. You've adapted to it and are used to being open with those you encounter. *But.* When it comes to discussing your chosen treatment—particularly when that treatment is a hot-button topic like marijuana—those questions and comments may suddenly fall beyond the scope of curiosity and good intentions. In fact, you might find yourself (dazedly) fending off passionate protests or angry accusations.

I don't tell you this to scare or discourage you. But it's important that you are prepared for how vicious other people can be when they encounter ideas that challenge their viewpoints, beliefs, or life experience. No matter how tough and resilient you already are (and I have no doubt that fighting to raise a chronically ill child has turned you into an absolute warrior!), it is always unsettling to face hostility and judgment from people who don't know you and don't truly understand your journey.

That said, I urge you to take these confrontations—when they happen—with a grain of salt. Many Americans tend to have a negative view of marijuana or "pot." But slowly, these prejudices are starting to lift as more people learn about this plant's beneficial properties. We are finally getting to a place where cannabis is being recognized as a medicine by the medical community, and the general public is also slowly starting to take notice. However, we still have a long way to go before the population at large accepts medical cannabis as a beneficial treatment for chronically ill children and adults.

Did you know?

U.S. Patent No. 6630507 was granted to the U.S. Department of Health and Human Services in 2003 and covers the potential use of non-psychoactive cannabinoids to protect the brain from damage or degeneration caused by certain diseases.

If you plan to treat your child's health condition or disease with medical cannabis, like it or not, you will find yourself at the forefront of this debate. I believe that's a good thing. After all, the only way to move forward and change people's attitudes is by being willing to speak up and educate people, so they are more open to treatments involving CBD-rich oil and other forms of medical cannabis. But it may not always be easy or fun to take on this task.

After everything we had already been through with RayAnn, it felt like a cruel joke when we finally found a miracle solution for her, but couldn't shout from the rooftops that she was better at last. Our community had always rallied around our family with such support that it was challenging to feel we couldn't immediately share our joy and new success with them as well. We desperately wanted to tell everyone about what we had discovered. But knowing how so many feel about marijuana, we were hesitant to reveal the source of her improvement.

In the end, we were very lucky in that we received mostly positive responses when we told people the truth. For the most part, everyone was always kind, even sympathetic. Those who knew RayAnn well and understood her story were open to medical cannabis as the next option we were trying (after having tried so many ineffective treatments beforehand). But even they couldn't fully comprehend what all we had been through, and what all we had tried prior to this point.

One factor that made our situation unique was our media exposure surrounding the topic. My husband and I had been working to pass the legislation legalizing medical cannabis in Florida, so our involvement was no big secret. Our work and the publicity surrounding it jumpstarted the conversation for us in many ways.

Your experience will surely be somewhat different from ours. You may recognize some of the themes from this book when you begin your own journey with medical cannabis. I hope you will stay confident as you share your child's treatment details with those in your circle, come what may. Remember that everything you're fighting for is more important than what your friends, neighbors, or random naysayers think about what you're doing. Do what's best for your loved one and remember these tips to help you along the way.

Know that when and how you tell people is completely up to you. You don't have to immediately tell everyone you meet that you're using medical cannabis to treat your chronically ill child. Choosing who to tell—and when to tell it—is completely up to you. When you are ready, select a few people you trust, like your immediate family, and start with them. Later on, as you feel more comfortable, you can expand the list of those "in the know" and share your news with others.

As mentioned, we initially chose to keep this information very quiet and told only our parents. But it didn't take long for people to notice that things were changing for RayAnn. My sister quickly noticed that RayAnn was improving, and so did her teachers. When it was clear that the time was right, we told them about her treatments. Remember, your family's timeline is the most important, so do what feels right to you. You should be honest with your doctor from the very beginning. Your physician should be made aware of changes in your child's treatment plan and should assist you through this process.

Understand that other people don't know your story. (They can't.) Only you have lived your story, and you alone understand the late nights, the scary moments, and the desperation to find a treatment that eases your child's suffering. Even if other people do know your story to some degree, they still don't *know* it. They haven't felt your fear each day. They don't know all the treatments you have tried along the way, and they can't know the relief you felt when you finally discovered something that worked. Try to remember this when you are met with opposition from outside people. They. Just. Don't. Know.

RayAnn was very sick—so sick we thought we might lose her. It seemed like a miracle when CBD-rich oil helped her get off her other powerful medicines and she started to thrive. Our family knew our truth so intimately that it seemed like black and white to us. You will likely see your child's situation in the same way, but other people probably won't feel the same way because they haven't lived your story. Having this intrinsic understanding goes a long way in helping you talk to others about your child's treatment.

Recognize that you don't know other people's stories either. It's important to understand that people's reactions come from their personal experiences. Try to keep this in mind as you disclose your child's treatment to others. One of the most common pushbacks we received centered around concerns about addiction. One gentleman at our church approached us and said, "I hope this works for RayAnn, but my fear is that I lost a brother to addiction."

He wasn't the only one who raised the addiction concern. Many other people told me about their family members or loved ones who had struggled with addiction. Concerned parents worried that if medical marijuana became legal, their teenaged children would have access to it. Again, people don't understand your child's struggles and the journey you've been on, but neither do you understand their journey. Approach conversations with this understanding and remember that most people aren't trying to deny your child treatments that will make them better. Rather, they are coming from a place of fear based on their own experiences.

Have your elevator speech ready to go. If you treat your child's chronic illness with medical cannabis, you have an obligation to give people an explanation if for no other reason than to educate them and make the way easier for future parents who need access to this treatment. The fact of the matter is, you will probably be explaining or justifying your child's treatment for the rest of your life. Accept this and know that it will get easier over time. It helps to have a well-rehearsed elevator speech ready that you can use whenever questions or confrontations arise. Be prepared to use it anywhere—schools, churches, playgrounds, grocery stores, gas stations, or wherever you go in your community.

A woman from our community approached me in the grocery store and told me she couldn't support what I was doing—treating my daughter with medical marijuana. I asked if she had a minute so I could try to explain. I gave her my "elevator speech," and sure enough, she softened and changed her mind on the spot. At the heart of the matter, this woman wanted to know that we were doing what was best for RayAnn.

When you are met with a question, the best way to answer is with a very measured, non-emotional response. Keep your answer simple and concise, and don't worry too much about convincing the other person that you are "right." No matter what you say, they still may not agree with you, but that's really not your problem. Just say "thanks for listening" and move on.

Tips for Your Elevator Speech

- Ask permission to explain.
- Keep it short and simple.
- Don't get emotional.
- Don't argue.
- Thank them for listening.

Be as open as possible with your inner circle. Your "inner circle" is made up of people who support and love you and your child, and want the best for your family. They are vital to your survival, and that is why it is key to keep this team, this support group that you've worked so hard to build, intact. The more they understand and feel included, the better. We have been especially lucky that the people we are close to have been very supportive of RayAnn's treatment with CBD-rich oil.

Once we became comfortable sharing RayAnn's treatment with a slightly larger group of people, it was important to us to make sure our friends, family, and the parents of our children's friends all knew that the type of oil RayAnn takes does *not* make her high (and does not make anyone else who would take it high, either). When friends came over to visit, I would show them the medicine and how we administer it. This helps them see that there is nothing to be afraid of. In fact, our home poses no greater risk than the risk associated with visiting a grandparent who might have multiple prescriptions in their medicine cabinet.

The more transparent you can be with your inner circle, the more they will support you and have your back. And believe me, you will be grateful for their on-going support over the years.

Encourage people to do their own research. It never hurts to have some resources or materials available that you can give people to read themselves, so they understand the uses and effects of medical cannabis. When you encounter someone with a lot of questions, answer them patiently but also encourage them to do their own research. Make it clear that you *want* them to know more about using cannabis products as medicine. The hope here is that people will realize you aren't trying to hide any information regarding your child's treatment, and will realize it isn't a "bad" thing. Dr. Sanjay Gupta's documentary *Weed* is a great starting point for anyone who wants to learn more. Another great resource is Dr. Bonni Goldstein's *Cannabis Revealed.*

Helpful Resources for People Who Want to Learn More

- Project CBD—www.projectcbd.org
- Realm of Caring—www.theroc.us
- Americans for Safe Access— www.safeaccessnow.org

Three Common Questions and How to Answer Them

Below are the three questions we most often received when people learned that we were using CBD-rich oil to treat RayAnn's epilepsy. You may frequently get asked these same questions. Feel free to try out these responses, which we have found to be very effective.

What are the long-term effects of treating your child with medical cannabis?

We honestly don't know what the long-term effects will be. But we do know what the long-term effects would be if our daughter continued to constantly have seizures. We also don't know the long-term effects of the Clonazepam that she took for years, which was an FDA-approved pharmaceutical.

Are you getting your child high?

No. RayAnn takes Charlotte's Web oil, which is high in CBD but extremely low in THC content (<0.3%). CBD, or cannabidiol, is considered safe and non-toxic to humans and will not cause you to experience a euphoric effect or "high." CBD-rich products provide the medicinal benefits of cannabis without the psychoactive effects.

Why would you give your child something that isn't FDA approved?

The truth is that many of the current pharmaceuticals that are FDA approved have harmful side effects that are known. There is a lot of research to suggest that medical cannabis is less harmful than many synthetic medicines that are currently on the market and being prescribed to patients. After thorough research and careful consideration, we have chosen this method of treatment for our child because we feel this is what works best for her. We encourage more research and hope that we can help to end the stigma behind medical cannabis so that FDA approval will one day be an option.

Be proactive in educating people (even if it takes you out of your comfort zone). Make spreading the word about the benefits of medical cannabis a family effort. The more people who understand the truth, the more we can erase the stigma surrounding medical cannabis use. Peyton and I made a goal to educate people by talking about medical cannabis to one person each day.

This came easy to Peyton, and he often talked to ten people in a day! I found it a little more challenging to push outside my comfort zone and broach the topic with others. But before long, I learned to get creative in my approach. For instance, I once pulled out a newspaper article about RayAnn and showed it to the clerk at the grocery store to get a conversation started. By the end of our exchange, not only the clerk, but also the bagger, and the person standing in line behind me had engaged in a positive conversation about medical cannabis use.

Know when to take somebody on, and when to let it go. There's a big difference between someone being disturbed yet curious about medical cannabis, and someone who is gunning for a fight. Usually, people are just looking for more information to reassure them that you are acting responsibly on behalf of your child. In most cases, they will be open-minded once you give them the facts and answer their questions. However, if you encounter someone who just wants to argue or becomes hostile, it's usually better not to engage too much. Don't stick around and try to "win" the argument; you'll just exhaust yourself and get upset. Instead, speak your piece respectfully and then walk away.

Don't take anything personally. At the end of the day, you know what's best for your child and your family. You can't let anyone's acceptance or lack of acceptance define your relationships. Remember that some people just aren't open to changing their views, and nothing you can do will make them change. What you *can* do is share your story openly and honestly, and see where it lands. The people who love your child will support you, and the people who can't get past decisions they don't agree with are not your problem.

Keep in mind that people come from many different places and have countless opinions that they will most certainly share with you. In the end, we all have to learn to respect one another and try to move forward with the facts at hand. The more people who understand where you're coming from, the easier it will be for medical cannabis to become an accessible solution for everyone who needs it. As members of the growing ranks of people who have enjoyed success with medical cannabis, it's our duty to share our stories—to finally give names and faces to this cause and help make meaningful change possible.

Chapter 10

Lobby for Your Cause

As the parent to a sick child, you would move Heaven and Earth to get them the help they need. I know that feeling well. When we discovered CBD-rich oil and saw for ourselves the miraculous results that families in Colorado were experiencing, we immediately began to think about what we could do to make it available to RayAnn. Of course, at the time, the obvious and most immediate choice was for us to move to Colorado where it was legal and readily available. I started to plan out how RayAnn and I might move and have Peyton and our younger children follow us later. But the reality was not that simple. The thought of splitting up our family, even temporarily, wasn't something we were thrilled about. Leaving our home also meant leaving our family and friends, the doctors who had worked with RayAnn and knew her history, and the teachers who had loved and nurtured her for so long. We had jobs in Florida. A home, a *life*.

The truth is that if Colorado had been the only option for us, I would have packed our bags and we would have figured out a way to make it work. We knew that this was what RayAnn needed and would have done whatever we had to do to make it happen for her. And unlike so many families, we were fortunate that we even had the means to move at all. For many families, it isn't feasible to leave jobs or sell homes or move across the country, which leaves countless patients stuck with little to no options for getting the treatment they need (and deserve!). In the end, we decided to stay where we were and fight to pass the legislation that would allow our daughter to have access to CBD-rich oil in our home state of Florida. I'll be honest—the journey wasn't an easy one, and there were times when I wondered if we would ever get the job done. We never gave up, and I am so proud of what we were able to accomplish for our family and for the state of Florida. When the Compassionate Medical Cannabis Act of 2014 was passed, it made high-CBD, low-THC cannabis oil a reality for RayAnn and so many others in our state who were suffering.

If you live in one of the states where medical cannabis isn't legal, taking charge in passing the legislation may be your next big step. Looking back on our experience, there are a few tips that I felt made a big difference for us along the way. As you read on, I hope you feel inspired and encouraged to take on this most important cause where you live.

Find (or create) a support group. Throughout this book I've stressed multiple times about the importance of a solid support system as one of the keys to survival in this journey. The same is true for tackling legislation and making change in the government. After all, the louder the voice, the more likely you are to be heard. Finding a support system of other people or families who also have the same goal in mind gives you the power of numbers. The more people in a state who are asking the same thing, the more likely your government officials will be willing to listen to you. Not only will your collective stories help to build the case, but being able to share some of the burden is a huge help as you go through this process.

Start small. The truth of the matter is that unless you are lucky enough to have a voice inside the government from the start, you're going to have to work really hard to get to that point. Don't let that discourage you. Instead, use the momentum you feel now to make a start in smaller venues, like local government or civic groups, where you can begin to bring attention to this issue and start to get a feel for anyone who may be a great ally down the road. You can also begin to create change right away by calling and emailing your local senators and representatives and asking for meetings. If you don't get an answer right away, keep trying. Reach out to community leaders who have political influence and relationships with legislators. This builds your army of voices and adds political strength to your message. You can also work to organize workshops and forums where other like-minded citizens can share their stories and collaborate on ideas for next steps.

Surround yourself with the right people. This is the most important piece of advice I can offer as we begin to talk about this topic. There are so many different facets of this process, and it is so unbelievably complex, that there is no way we would have been able to accomplish what we did on our own. It took partnering with the right people, people who had a working knowledge and expertise of government, medical cannabis, and media to make our success happen. I highly recommend finding a lobbyist to partner with who can help to get you in front of the right people (they already have established relationships!) and go to those meetings with you. If at all possible, finding a partner inside the government itself is a huge win, especially if with the majority party. We were lucky to be able to work with

Representative Matt Gaetz, who was well-respected by the majority party and had much influence with leadership. And lastly, partnering with someone who can guide you through media interviews and help you to prepare your talking points is a game changer!

Plan (and practice!) what you will say. If you get a meeting with a legislator, know going in that they work on a very busy schedule. Your time will likely be short, which means you will have to get your point across quickly and concisely. Know whom it is you are meeting with. (For example: Are they a parent? Are they in the healthcare field? Have they previously voted on a bill that helped children you could thank them for up front?) If the member isn't from your area, be sure and have a family from his or her area reach out to them or have them to join you in the meeting. Remember, they care about their constituents the most! Think about how this issue will impact them back home and use that as you develop your talking points.

As you get further into the process, you'll find yourself in a lot of face-to-face meetings with different people and you'll be telling your story over and over (and over!) again. Draft your "elevator" speech and practice, practice, practice. Be honest, sincere, and passionate, but steer away from being overly emotional or angry. (Trust me, I know how difficult this can be! There is nothing as passionate as a parent fighting to protect their child!) Having this speech fine-tuned will be helpful for any speaking opportunities or media interviews that may come up down the road. Most importantly, make sure that your speech doesn't just tell the story of what has happened to you or share your grievance, but that it ends with a solution. You want to provide something that these people can do, which in turn helps them to take your request and put it into action!

Tips for Meeting With Your Elected Officials

- Be on time for your appointment.

- Arrive with a prepared handout and photos that you can leave with them. (A one-pager is best as their time and attention are both short!)

- Have a condensed version of your speech ready to go. (Appointment time is limited!)

- Follow up with a handwritten and personal thank-you.

- Be honest, sincere, and passionate but steer away from being overly emotional or angry.

- Have a solution in hand to offer.

- If you are meeting with a legislator who doesn't live in your area, find a family from their area who will attend with you or share their story.

- Take notes!

Make it personal. It is so important to put a face on the fight you are fighting. Letting lawmakers, lobbyists, and even the local cashier know that this issue is real and it affects real people is paramount to changing minds and making headway. When people can *see* the children who are using this and having success, and can put a name and face to the issue at hand, it makes them more likely to work toward a solution. When we were working to pass the legislation in Florida, I made a photo collage of RayAnn and carried it with me to every meeting. I showed them the photos of our daughter, as a sick and helpless child, in the hospital, and then the photos of her looking healthy and happy as a shining example of why this bill was so desperately needed. I wanted them to remember her precious face in their minds when they were voting or speaking to their colleagues or constituents.

Leave them with something to remember you by. While it's a huge win to just get in front of some of these decision-makers, you also want to make sure that they will remember you, and your request, once you're no longer sitting in their office. Having a small "leave-behind" is a great way to keep your cause and your ask in front of them as a gentle reminder. We had bracelets made with our hashtag, #IStandWithRayAnn, and the bill number on them, and we would leave them with the people we were meeting with in order to keep her name and the bill on their mind after our face-to-face time was over.

Social Media Savvy

Social media can play a huge role in spreading the word and gaining support when you are working on new legislation. A catchy, meaningful name for your campaign makes it easy to remember and recognize. We created "I Stand With RayAnn," which we also used as our hashtag for social media sites like Twitter.

Follow up with a meaningful thank-you. Again, you've likely had to work hard to get in front of these decision-makers, and you don't want your time with them to be lost in the long list of things they already have going on. Sending a personal thank-you after your meeting is a great way to have them lay eyes on your cause a second time—and the more meaningful and powerful you can make that thank-you the better. Consider having your child write or sign the letter, or draw a picture. Include a photo, thank them for taking the time to meet with you, offer to help in any way you can, and be sure to remind them of the solution you offered at the meeting.

When we were going through this process, we had RayAnn make paintings that we gave to the legislators as a "thank-you" for meeting with us and taking on our cause. In fact, we had an in-person meeting with Governor Rick Scott, and RayAnn was able to hand-deliver the painting she made for him. He made her a personal promise that he would sign the bill into a law. It was a very special moment for our family!

Be confident. I know how intimidating it can feel to walk into a room full of "important people" with the weight of your child's health and future sitting squarely on your shoulders. The stakes are high, the time is short, and you want to make sure you utilize every second you have to get your point across and Make. It. Happen. I want you to know that one person *can* make a difference. Your opinion matters. Yes, we do need these policymakers to write the bills and change the laws, but remember that they need us, too. We are the ones who have lived this story, who have raised and fought for these kids. We know this better than anyone else, and they need us to be the voice of change to help our children and countless other patients who don't have access to lifesaving medicine. Be confident in your story, in what you know, and what you are fighting for.

Have patience, patience, patience. I know. I KNOW. You've come this far, you've fought this long, and now it's something like governmental red tape holding you back from the thing you've been hoping and praying for all this time. I understand how your patience may be at an all-time low and now you're being asked to wait again. The thing is, whether we like it or not, nothing moves quickly in government. To say it is a long process would be an understatement. It took us years to get to the point where we are today, and honestly we still aren't done! Every single time you think you're done, it seems another process will be waiting to start. The process will be long and the results won't be immediate, but I promise your patience will pay off in the end. Stay the course; don't give up!

As the parent to a sick child, you already know what it takes to be a fighter, an advocate, and someone who never gives up. This means you already possess the three most important qualities you need as you take on this next battle in this journey. Keep your eye on the goal ahead: real and lasting change that will affect you and countless others for the better. As you well know, it isn't always going to be easy, but it will always be worth it.